Timesaver
Vocabulary Activities
(Elementary)

Teacher's reference key

A small clock on each page tells you approximately
how long each activity should take.

Individual

Pair

Group

Small icons at the top of each page show whether
the activity is best suited to individual, pair or group work.

Timesaver Vocabulary Activities
(Elementary)

CONTENTS

My Family

Complete the crossword.

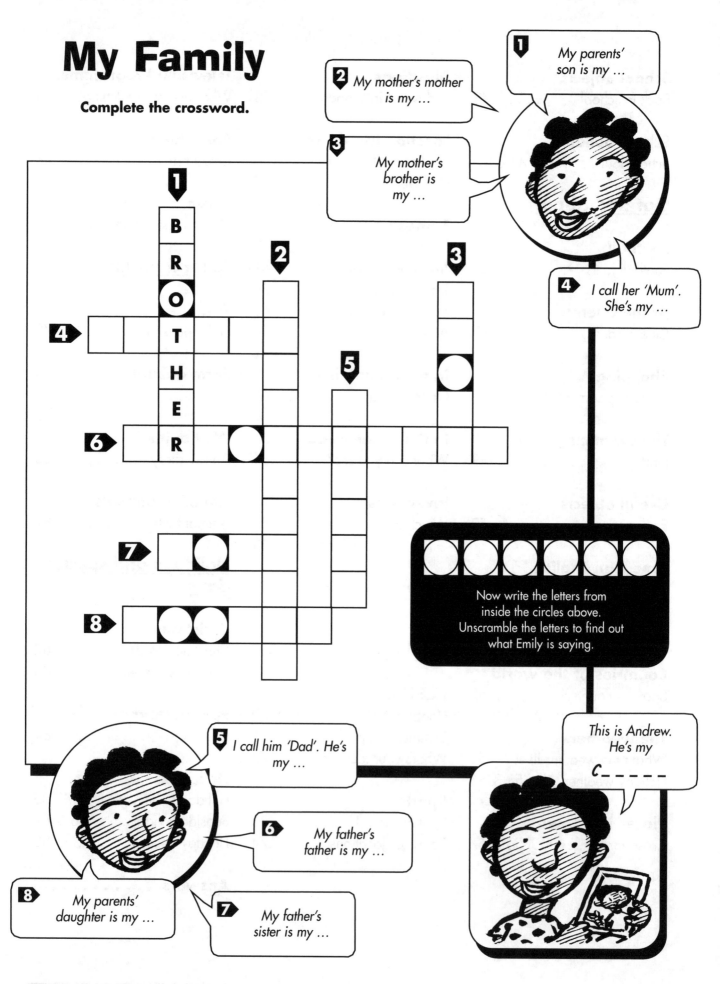

1 My parents' son is my ...

2 My mother's mother is my ...

3 My mother's brother is my ...

4 I call her 'Mum'. She's my ...

5 I call him 'Dad'. He's my ...

6 My father's father is my ...

7 My father's sister is my ...

8 My parents' daughter is my ...

Now write the letters from inside the circles above. Unscramble the letters to find out what Emily is saying.

This is Andrew. He's my c _ _ _ _ _

Family Tree

This is Coco the Clown and his family.
Read the information and write the names to complete the family tree.

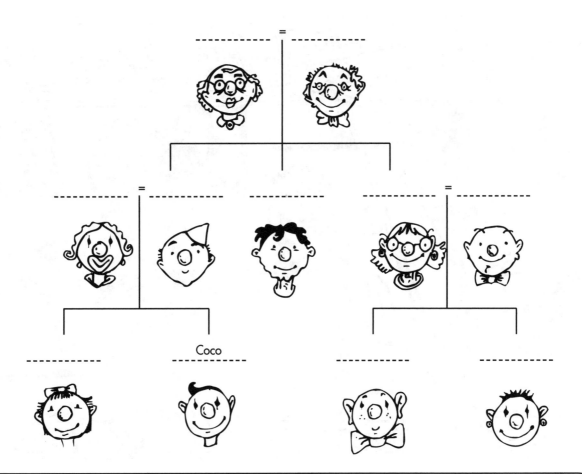

Coco

★ Coco's sister is called Clara.
★ Their mother is Connie.
★ Her husband is Joey.
★ Coco's grandfather is Joey's father.
His name is Dino.

★ Dino has got two sons. One is called Bozo.
★ Coco's grandmother is Esmerelda.
★ Esmerelda has got a daughter called Dolly.

★ Dolly has got a son called Matt.
★ Marvin's wife is Dolly.
★ Coco has got a cousin called Molly.

Who is wrong?

I've got two uncles and an aunt.

I've got three children and four grandchildren.

I've got a wife, a son and a daughter.

I've got two brothers and two cousins.

Football Training

Today is football training and you've got the shirts for the youth club football team.

Who gets which number? Read the sentences and write a number on each player's shirt.

① **Player number 1** is tall and quite fat. He's got long, straight black hair. He doesn't wear glasses.

② **Player number 2** is short and quite fat. Her hair is medium-length, dark and curly.

③ **Player number 3** has got dark hair, too. His hair is short and straight. He's short and very thin.

④ **Player number 4** is slim and quite short. She wears glasses. She's got long, curly blond hair.

⑤ **Player number 5** has also got blond hair. His hair is straight and medium-length. He's tall and fat and doesn't wear glasses.

⑥ **Player number 6** is also tall and quite fat. He's got short, blond curly hair.

⑦ **Player number 7** is tall and slim. She doesn't wear glasses. She's got long, straight, brown hair.

⑧ **Player number 8** has also got brown hair but her hair is medium-length and curly. She's tall and slim.

⑨ **Player number 9** is quite short and quite fat. He's got short, straight blond hair and he wears glasses.

⑩ **Player number 10** doesn't wear glasses. She's tall with medium-length, curly blond hair.

⑪ **Player number 11** has got short, black hair. She's tall and quite slim.

The referee hasn't got a number on his shirt. Draw a circle around the referee. Then write a description of him.

Wanted!

Oxford City police have got photos of twelve suspects in a robbery.

Choose a suspect. Don't tell your partner which suspect it is!
In pairs, ask a maximum of ten questions each to find out which suspect you chose.
Example: Has he got glasses? (Yes, he has. / No, he hasn't.)
Has he got small ears? (Yes, he has. / No, he hasn't.)

Choose another suspect and write a description. Your partner reads your description and finds the suspect.

The Monster

Write the names of the parts of the body. Use the words in the box.

head	ear	eye	nose	mouth	chin
arm	hand	stomach	leg	~~foot~~	

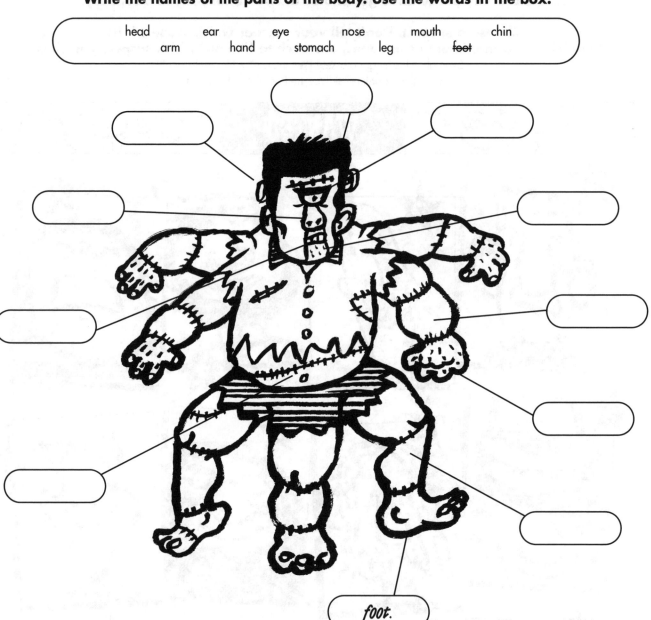

foot.

What has the monster got? Write True or False.

1	He's got one eye.

True.

3	He's got three feet.

5	He's got two chins.

2	He's got two ears.

4	He's got one nose.

Now write five more sentences about the monster.

Personality Spiral

Write the adjectives in the box in the correct place on the spiral.

The first letter of each adjective is already on the spiral.

brave

clever

funny

generous

~~happy~~

honest

mad

patient

polite

rude

selfish

shy

sociable

stupid

talkative

Now write the letters from inside the circles.

Unscramble the letters to find
an adjective to describe the alien.

I'm

f _ _ _ _ _ _ _

Find the opposites of these words in the spiral.

1	sad	*happy*	3	impatient	_____
2	mean	_____	4	cowardly	_____
			5	polite	_____

How sensitive are you?

Complete the personality quiz.

1

There's a new boy in your class. He's very quiet. What do you think?
- 🐝 He's shy. Perhaps he's sad.
- ☆ It's OK. Some people aren't very talkative.
- ☀ He's very rude!

3

The bus is late. How do you feel?
- ☀ Impatient and angry. Stupid bus!
- ☆ A bit impatient.
- 🐝 Worried – perhaps there's a problem with the bus.

2

Your mother is very tired. What do you say?
- ☀ Don't be lazy!
- 🐝 Let me help you! Really, I insist!
- ☆ Can I help you?

4

A friend finds some money in the street and she puts it in her pocket. What do you think?
- 🐝 That's OK – she hasn't got a lot of money.
- ☀ She's selfish. She should give me some money!
- ☆ She isn't very honest – whose money is it?

5

Your neighbour's dog is ill. What do you say?
- ☆ Don't worry. I'm sure he'll be better soon.
- 🐝 That's really terrible. Try to be brave.
- ☀ Don't be stupid, it's only a dog!

6

Which do you prefer to be?
- 🐝 polite
- ☆ friendly
- ☀ funny

Add up your points and check your results.

12 points or less: You aren't very sensitive and sometimes you can be rude. Try to think of other people and be more thoughtful.

13 – 20 points: You're a friendly, sociable person. You're honest and quite generous. Sometimes you're sensitive, but try to think of others a bit more often.

21 – 30 points: You're polite, generous and very sensitive. You aren't selfish and you always think of others. Did you answer the questions honestly?!

POINTS
🐝 = 5 points
☆ = 3 points
☀ = 1 point

How old are you?

Read the sentences. Tick True or False.

Balvir

I'm eleven.
My birthday's on the
19th of March.

Gina

I'm twelve.
My birthday's on
St Valentine's Day –
the 14th of February.

Lauren

I'm twelve.
My birthday's in the
summer. It's on the
2nd of August.

Anna

I'm fourteen.
My birthday is on
the 25th of June.
I love birthdays!

Danny

I'm thirteen.
My birthday's in
the winter. It's on the
19th of December.

Scott

I'm thirteen and
my birthday's on the
21st of October.

	True	False
a. Balvir is 11.	☑	☐
b. Scott is 13.	☐	☐
c. Lauren is 14.	☐	☐
d. Gina's birthday is on the 14th of February.	☐	☐
e. Anna's birthday is on the 27th of July.	☐	☐
f. Danny's birthday is in December.	☐	☐
g. Lauren's birthday is in summer.	☐	☐
h. Balvir's birthday is in autumn.	☐	☐
i. Anna's birthday is in summer.	☐	☐
j. Both boys are 13.	☐	☐
k. Two of the girls are 14.	☐	☐
l. Scott's birthday is in autumn.	☐	☐
m. St Valentine's day is in February.	☐	☐
n. Gina and Lauren are 12.	☐	☐
o. Danny's birthday is in spring.	☐	☐
p. December is in winter.	☐	☐

Colour the picture to find out how old Lauren's cat is.

● If the statement is true, colour the section of the picture black.

○ If the statement is false, leave the section white.

Lauren's cat is _____

Inventions

Do you know the origin of these inventions?

Look at the pictures and read the sentences. Choose the correct nationality.

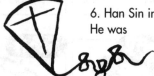

Example:
1. The first video games were

Japanese. [A] ✔ ...
Norwegian. [B] ...

2. The first guitar was

Spanish. [M] ...
Scottish. [E] ...

6. Han Sin invented the kite. He was

English. [N] ...
Chinese. [C] ...

3. The first hamburgers were

German. [E] ...
American. [B] ...

7. The man who made the first sandwich was

English. [A] ...
French. [H] ...

4. The company that first produced the mini-disc in 1992 was

Indian. [I] ...
Japanese. [R] ...

8. Cesare Bertana made the first postcard in 1865. Bertana was

Italian. [N] ...
Portuguese. [L] ...

5. The man who invented Lego® bricks was

Russian. [E] ...
Danish. [I] ...

Write the letters of the eight correct answers to finish the nationality word that completes this sentence

The first jukeboxes were   *A* _ _ _ _ _ _ _
1 2 3 4 5 6 7 8

Puzzle It Out!

These kids at the fair have each won a giant teddy bear.
Read the clues and fill in the names on the board.

- One girl feels happy, but it's not Anna.
- The girl called Carly feels thirsty.
- The boy called Daniel feels sad.
- Robbie feels sick.
- Elena doesn't feel tired.
- Simon feels hungry.

They smell delicious

Can I have a drink?

That was hard work!

You've won again

You've lost again

Ugh! That rollercoaster was too fast!

WINNERS OF THE DAY

1. [ ] _____
2. [ ] _____
3. [ ] _____
4. [ ] _____
5. [ ] _____
6. [ ] _____

The first letters of the names spell out how Luke feels!

Luke feels _ _ _ _ _ _ _ !

Feeling ill

What's wrong with the monster?
Cross out the words in the grid and write them next to each picture.

Oh, doctor!
I have a terrible ...

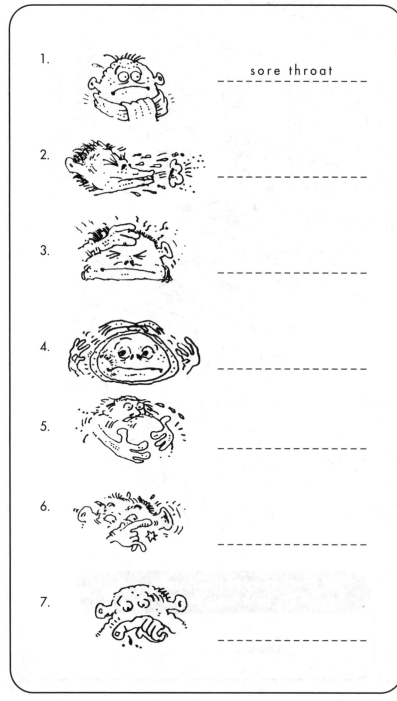

1. _ _ _ _ sore throat _ _ _ _ _ _

2. _ _ _ _ _ _ _ _ _ _ _ _ _ _ _

3. _ _ _ _ _ _ _ _ _ _ _ _ _ _ _

4. _ _ _ _ _ _ _ _ _ _ _ _ _ _ _

5. _ _ _ _ _ _ _ _ _ _ _ _ _ _ _

6. _ _ _ _ _ _ _ _ _ _ _ _ _ _ _

7. _ _ _ _ _ _ _ _ _ _ _ _ _ _ _

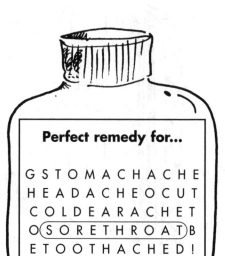

Perfect remedy for...

G S T O M A C H A C H E
H E A D A C H E O C U T
C O L D E A R A C H E T
O S O R E T H R O A T B
E T O O T H A C H E D !

Use the other letters to find out what the doctor says!

_ _ _ _ _ _ _ _ _ _

In my opinion...

What do these people think about these hobbies?
Match each sentence to the correct picture.

Fishing is relaxing   Reading is interesting   Shopping is great fun   Parachuting is exciting

Parachuting is frightening   Shopping is irritating   Fishing is boring   Reading is OK

1. _____!

2. _____!

3. _____!

4. _____!

5. _____!

6. _____!

7. _____!

8. _____!

What do you think about these hobbies? Write a sentence for each.

Telling the Time

Play the game with a friend.

AIM:
To reach FINISH before your friend.

YOU NEED:
One die, two counters.

51	52	53	54	55 *What time is it now?*
50	49	48	47 *What time do you get up in the morning?*	46
31	32	33	34	35
30	29	28	27 *What time do you eat breakfast?*	26
11 *What time do you arrive at school?*	12	13	14	15
10	9	8	7	6

Telling the Time

HOW TO PLAY:

1. Put your counters on START. Take turns to throw the die and move along the track.
2. If you land on a clock, say the time (or miss the next go!).
3. If you land on a question, your friend reads out the question and you answer it (or miss the next go!).
4. If you land on an arrow, move back.

				FINISH
56	57	58	59	60
45	44	43	42	41
36 *What time do you have lunch?*	37	38	39	40
25	24	23	22	21
16	17	18	19 *What time do you finish school?*	20
5 *What time do you go to bed?*	4	3	2	1
				START

Opening and Closing Times

<u>Student A</u>

You and your partner are in Bigtown for the day. You must go to the bank, the chemist's, the post office and the tourist office. You have a tourist leaflet but some of the opening and closing times are missing. Ask your partner questions to find the missing information.

What time does the bank open?

You must answer your partner's questions.

WELCOME TO BIGTOWN-ON-SEA!

	OPENING TIME	CLOSING TIME
bank	....	4pm
tourist office	9.30am	....
castle	....	7.30pm
post office	9am	....
supermarket	....	....
chemist's	8.30am	6pm
department store	9am	....
library	....	....
museum	10.30am	6pm
cinema	....	11.30pm
bowling alley	....	11.30pm
swimming pool	7am	....
sports centre	7am	....
theme park	10.30am	8pm
zoo	10.30am	8.30pm
disco	....	2am

Arrange your programme for the day. Decide on 4 more places to visit. When will you visit each place? Make a list.

Opening and Closing Times

Student B

You and your partner are in Bigtown for the day. You must go to the bank, the chemist's, the post office and the tourist office. You have a tourist leaflet but some of the opening and closing times are missing. Ask your partner questions to find the missing information.

What time does the bank close?

You must answer your partner's questions.

WELCOME TO BIGTOWN-ON-SEA!		
	OPENING TIME	**CLOSING TIME**
bank	9am	....
tourist office	....	5.30pm
castle	11am	....
post office	....	5pm
supermarket	8.30am	11pm
chemist's	....	....
department store	....	5pm
library	9am	8pm
museum	....	....
cinema	2.30pm	....
bowling alley	3.30pm	....
swimming pool	....	9.45pm
sports centre	....	9.45pm
theme park	....	....
zoo	....	....
disco	7.30pm	....

Arrange your programme for the day. Decide on 4 more places to visit. When will you visit each place? Make a list.

Dates for your calendar

Read what Ranjit says about these special days and write them on the calendar.

JANUARY	FEBRUARY	MARCH
APRIL	MAY	JUNE
JULY	AUGUST *3rd Ranjit's Birthday*	SEPTEMBER
OCTOBER	NOVEMBER	DECEMBER

My birthday: *It's on the 3rd of the month before September. This year I am 14.*
Christmas Day: *It's on the 25th of the last month of the year. We send cards and get presents.*
Bonfire Night: *It's on the 5th of the month before December. In the park, there is a bonfire and fireworks.*
Diwali: *It's the Hindu festival of light. This year, it's the month before November. We have a big party.*
New Year's Day: *It's the first day of the first month of the year. I stay up very late the night before.*
Valentine's Day: *It's the 14th of the month after January. I'm going to send a card to a girl I like.*
Exams start: *At school my exams start on the 10th of the month after April. Oh no!*
Summer holidays start: *School finishes on 24th of the month before August. Yes!!!*
Mother's Day: *I'm going to send my mum a card in the month before April.*
Father's Day: *I'm going to send my dad a card in the month after May.*

Add some more important dates to the calendar (Easter, Spring holiday, Halloween, your birthday, family and friends' birthdays, etc.).

Numbers Picture

How many of the things in the list can you find?

monkeys — *There are* _____ *three monkeys* _____

sea lions — _____

zoo-keepers — _____

elephants — _____

clouds — _____

trees — _____

lions — _____

dustbins — _____

butterflies — _____

birds — _____

children — _____

Collection Crazy!

Play the game with a friend.

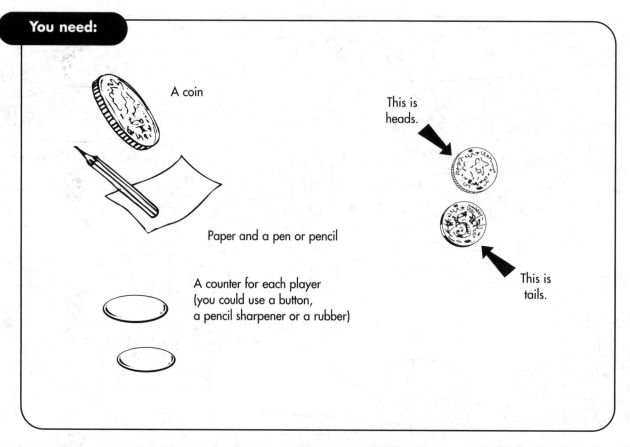

You need:

A coin

Paper and a pen or pencil

A counter for each player
(you could use a button,
a pencil sharpener or a rubber)

This is
heads.

This is
tails.

Aims:

You want to build up a stamp and coin collection. The winner is the player who collects most coins and stamps.

How to play:

1. Both players put their counters on the START square.
2. Player 1: toss the coin. Heads or tails? Follow the arrow and move your counter. Say what you've got.
3. Write it on your paper.

4. Player 2 does the same.
5. Take turns to play.
6. Keep a running total.
7. The winner is the person with the most stamps and coins when one person has reached the finish.

I've got five stamps.

coins | stamps

5

*Ten stamps! Now
I've got
twenty-one stamps.*

coins | stamps

4 | 11
| 21

Collection Crazy!

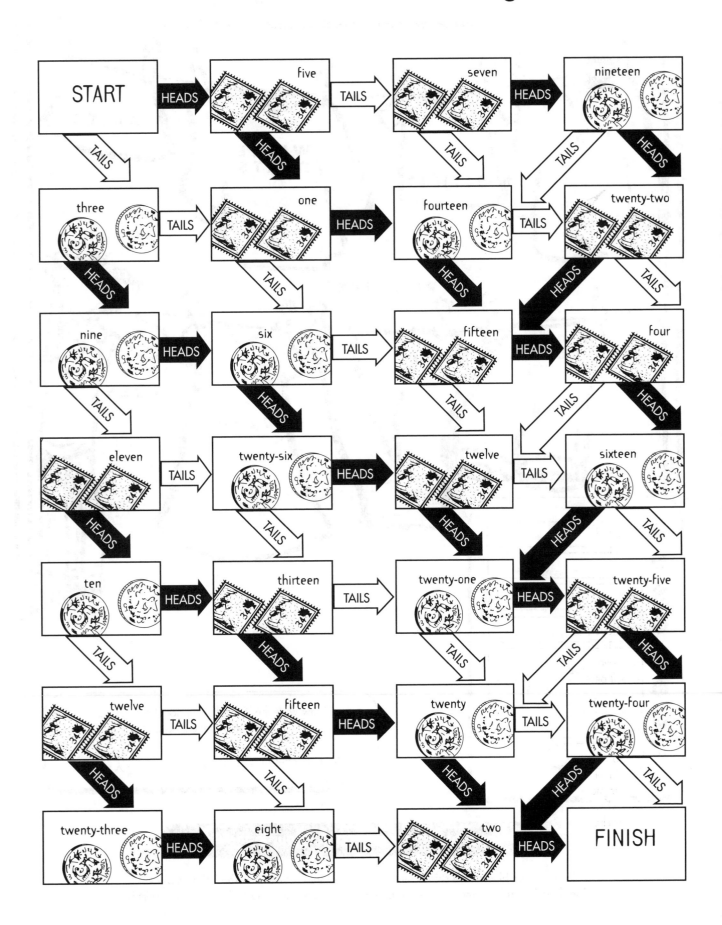

On the Washing Line

Unscramble the letters and write the names of the clothes.

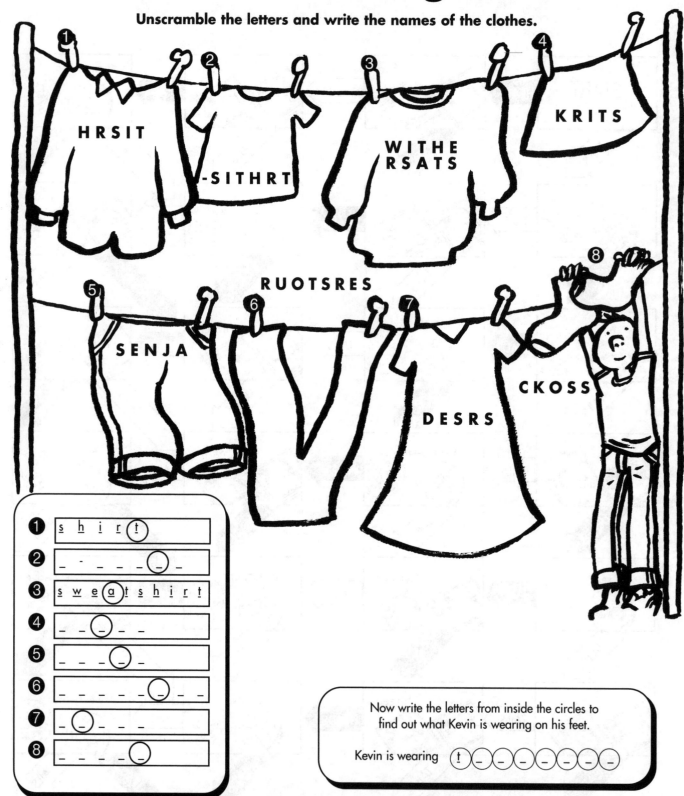

Now write the letters from inside the circles to
find out what Kevin is wearing on his feet.

Kevin is wearing ⓣ ◯ - ◯ - ◯ - ◯ - ◯

Now read the sentences and colour in the clothes.

The jeans are blue.   The shirt is pink.   The sweatshirt is yellow.   The T-shirt is black.
The dress is purple.   The trousers are brown.   The socks are blue and white.   The skirt is red.

Hide and Seek

Read the descriptions. Who's hiding behind the tree?
Write the names next to the people.

• Peter is wearing a white T-shirt, a bomber jacket, black trousers and black shoes.

• Paul is wearing a cap, a white shirt, a jumper, jeans and trainers.

• Laura is wearing a white skirt, a jumper and white shoes.

• Sophie is wearing a white shirt, a grey skirt, a leather jacket and sandals.

Now draw the other two people hiding behind the second tree.

Eurocolours

Colour by numbers.
Colour these fifteen European flags

a. *Austria*

1
2
1

1 red **2** white **3** black **4** yellow **5** blue **6** green **7** orange

b. _ _ _ _ _ _ _

3	4	1

c. _ _ _ _ _ _ _

1		1
	2	
1		1

d. _ _ _ _ _ _ _

2		2
	5	
2		2

e. _ _ _ _ _ _

5	2	1

f. _ _ _ _ _ _ _

3
1
4

g. _ _ _ _ _ _

5		5	2
	2		5
5		5	2

(repeating 5 / 2 / 5 / 2 / 5)

h. _ _ _ _ _ _ _

6	2	7

i. _ _ _ _ _

6	2	1

j. _ _ _ _ _ _ _

1
2
5

k. _ _ _ _ _ _ _

1
2
5

l. _ _ _ _ _ _

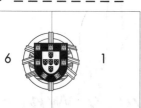

6   1

m. _ _ _ _ _ _

1
4
1

n. _ _ _ _ _ _

5	5
4	
5	5

o. _ _ _ _ _ _ _ _ _ _

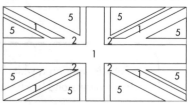

Now write the name of each country. Use the words in the box.

Netherlands	Belgium	United Kingdom	~~Austria~~	Finland
Luxembourg	Ireland	Germany	Denmark	Greece
Italy	Portugal	France	Sweden	Spain

Helping Out at Home

Are you a SUPER HELPER?

Look at the chores. Put a tick (✔) if you answer 'Yes' and a cross (✗) if you answer 'No'.
If you put a tick, look at the pictures and collect your tokens.
If you put a cross, you get no tokens and no points!

Chore	Yes	No	Token
I make my bed.			
I tidy up my bedroom.			
I vacuum the house.			
I dust the furniture.			
I go shopping.			
I do the cooking.			
I lay the table.			
I do the washing up.			
I look after the pets.			

Now count your tokens and read the results!

Ⓐ = 1   Ⓑ = 2   Ⓒ = 3

- You have less than 6 points:
Not bad! But you can do a bit more to help! Ask your
mum and dad!
- You have more than 6 points:
Congratulations, you win the SUPER HELPER badge!

Fruity Fun!

Find the fruit in the grid.
Write the correct name under each fruit.

orange
....

....

....

....

O	P	D	O	Y	G	O	C
R	U	E	L	I	R	K	H
A	P	E	A	S	A	T	E
N	K	L	R	R	P	A	R
G	I	W	U	B	E	E	R
E	W	R	R	M	S	I	I
E	I	A	P	P	L	E	E
B	A	N	A	N	A	S	S

....

....

....

....

....

Use the other letters in the grid to write the worm's question.

__ ___ ____ _____?

What is your favourite fruit?

_____

Picnic Crossword

Look at Nicky's picnic. Fill in the grid.

Nicky forgot her favourite food. Rearrange the letters in the grey squares to find out what it is.

Which Shop?

Move around the hexagons in the correct order to find the names of the shops.
Write the names on the shops.

Health Quiz

How healthy are you? To complete the quiz, look at the phrases below and write them next to the correct picture.

1. eat fruit and vegetables
2. walk to school
3. eat cakes and biscuits
4. smoke
5. drink fizzy drinks
6. watch TV

7. do sport
8. ride a bike
9. go swimming
10. go to bed early

Now do the quiz to find out if you have a healthy lifestyle. Circle the correct number. Add up the points in every square you circled and find out your total score. Read the analysis. Do you agree with it? Why? / Why not?

How often do you ...?

	Never	Sometimes	Every day
a. eat fruit and vegetables	0	1	2
b.	3	2	1
c.	0	1	2
d.	0	1	2
e.	3	1	0
f.	0	1	2
g.	2	1	0
h.	0	1	2
i.	2	1	0
j.	0	1	2

Analysis

18 or more: You are a very healthy person. You like to keep fit and you want to live a long life.

12-17: You want to be healthy and fit, but you like food that isn't good for you, and are sometimes a bit lazy.

6-11: You need to take your diet and exercise more seriously.

5 and under: You are very lazy! You don't care about what you eat or do to keep fit and healthy. Be careful! Change your lifestyle before it is too late!

Choose a job!

Look at the jobs in the box. Match them with the correct picture and write them on the lines.
To find your ideal job, choose your best subject at school, answer the questions and follow the arrows.

translator
accountant
editor
tour guide
actor
sports teacher
marine biologist
newspaper reporter
physiotherapist
~~maths teacher~~
town planner
doctor
film director
farmer

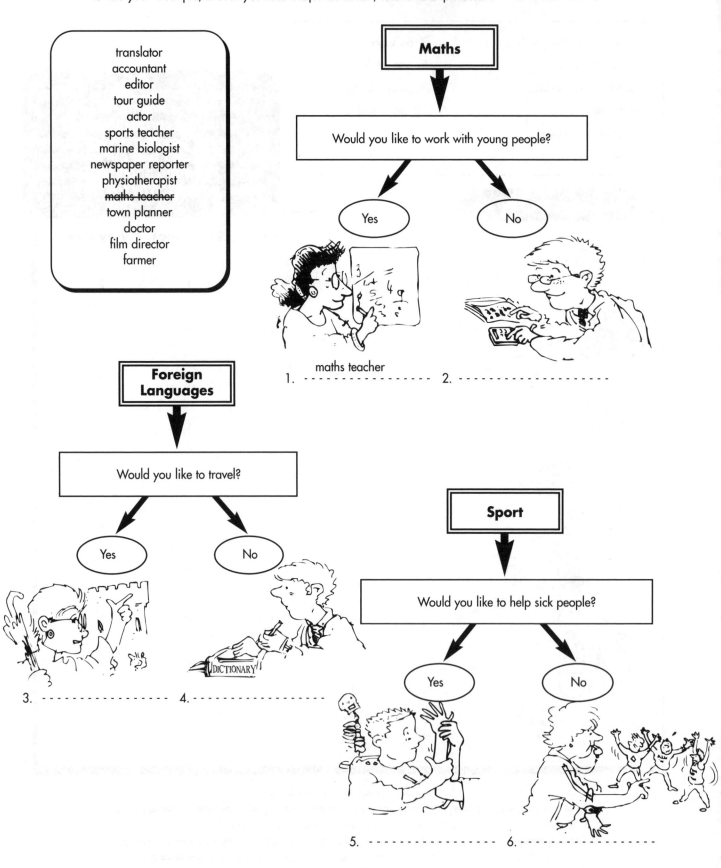

Maths

Would you like to work with young people?

Yes   No

maths teacher
1. - - - - - - - - - - - - - - -   2. - - - - - - - - - - - - - - -

Foreign Languages

Would you like to travel?

Yes   No

3. - - - - - - - - - - - - - - -   4. - - - - - - - - - - - - - - -

Sport

Would you like to help sick people?

Yes   No

5. - - - - - - - - - - - - - - -   6. - - - - - - - - - - - - - - -

Choose a job!

Science

↓

Would you like to work with animals?

↙ ↘

(Yes) (No)

9. - - - - - - - - - - - - - - - 10. - - - - - - - - - - - - - - -

Literature

↓

Would you like to work in an office?

↙ ↘

(Yes) (No)

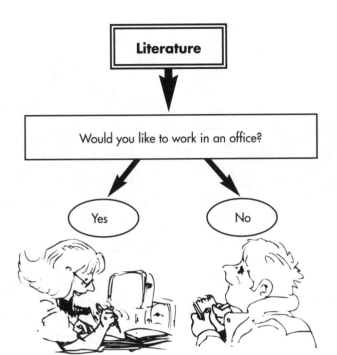

7. - - - - - - - - - - - - - - 8. - - - - - - - - - - - - - - -

Geography

↓

Would you like to work outside?

↙ ↘

(Yes) (No)

13. - - - - - - - - - - - - - 14. - - - - - - - - - - - - - -

Music and Drama

↓

Would you like to perform in front of an audience?

↙ ↘

(Yes) (No)

11. - - - - - - - - - - - - - 12. - - - - - - - - - - - - - -

Which jobs suits you and why?

Who lives where?

Read the information and write the names.

Adam's home is at the end of the street. He lives on the fifth floor.

Danielle lives in a cottage, next door to Joe.

Jill lives in a mobile home, opposite Danielle.

Oliver lives in a flat, next door to Lisa and opposite Adam.

Michelle lives in a bungalow next door to the mobile home.

Mark lives in a large, modern house next door to Adam and opposite Lisa.

Which sentence is wrong?

1

Joe lives in a small, modern house.

2

Jill lives next door to Michelle.

Lisa lives in a flat.

3

Where's Harry the hamster?

**Follow the instructions to each room to find Harry.
Start in the hall.**

In Lee's Bedroom

Student A

Label the picture with the words from the list.

~~bed~~	computer	rug	bookshelf
lamp	chair	wardrobe	alarm clock
poster	curtains	chest of drawers	mirror
desk		bedside table	

bed

Laura and Lee are friends. Laura has a birthday present for Lee. It is hidden in her bedroom.
Your partner has a picture of Laura's bedroom. Laura and Lee's bedrooms are very similar. Ask your partner questions to find out where the present is. Use *on, in, under, near, behind.*

In Laura's Bedroom

Student B

Label the picture with the words from the list.

~~bed~~	computer	wardrobe	bookshelf
lamp	chair	chest of drawers	alarm clock
poster	rug	bedside table	mirror
desk		curtains	

bed

Laura and Lee are friends. Lee has a birthday present for Laura. It is hidden in his bedroom.
Your partner has a picture of Lee's bedroom. Laura and Lee's bedrooms are very similar. Ask your partner
questions to find out where the present is. Use *on, in, under, near, behind.*

Mystery Objects

Look at the mystery objects. What are they? Circle a, b or c.

①
a. cooker

b. fridge

c. washing machine

②
a. toaster

b. tin opener

c. food mixer

③
a. sink

b. washing machine

c. microwave oven

④
a. dustpan

b. bowl

c. saucepan

⑤
a. vacuum cleaner

b. dustpan

c. broom

⑥
a. kettle

b. teapot

c. tap

How many of the kitchen objects mentioned in the exercise above can you find in this picture?

Picture Crossword

Complete the crossword.

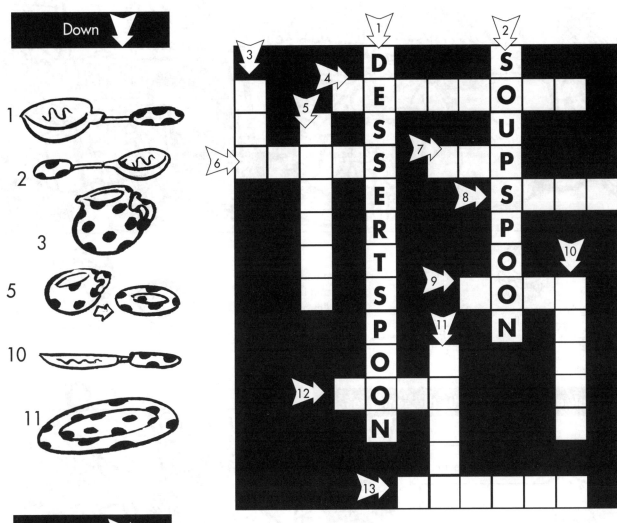

Down

1
2
3
5
10
11

Across

4
6
7
8
9
12
13

Vampire scare!

Look at picture A. Who is speaking? Match the faces with the texts.

cat

Bella

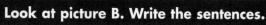
fish

1. I'm under the table.
2. I'm in the armchair.
3. I'm on the sofa.
4. I'm behind the curtain.
5. I'm next to the fireplace.
6. I'm in front of the TV.

Billy

Grandma

Grandpa

Look at picture B. Write the sentences.

I'm in the fireplace.

Find the Bag!

The teachers have lost their bags!
Match the teachers with the bags.
Example: a) Geography

English

French

Biology

Technology

History

Geography

General science

IT (Information Technology)

PE (Physical Education)

Maths

Art

RE (Religious Education)

Choose the best name for each teacher.
Use a dictionary if necessary.

Examples:
Ms Belief – RE
Mr Metal – Technology
Mr Leaf – Biology

	Mr Numbers	Ms Croissant	Ms X-ray
Mr Cambridge		Ms Portrait	Ms Past
	Mr Metal		Mr Globe
Mr Leaf	Ms Belief	Mr Keyboard	Ms Marathon

School Timetable

Read the clues and complete Kieran's timetable.

- Kieran's favourite subjects are technology and science.

- He's got a double lesson of one of his favourite subjects on Friday.

- He's always got English in lesson 4 except Wednesday and Thursday.

- He's got one of his favourite subjects on Monday lesson 1 and Thursday lesson 3 after French and before history.

- On Monday, he's got IT and then PE.

- He's got one lesson of RE a week, on Tuesday after history and before English.

- He's got three maths lessons – on Tuesday, on Wednesday after art and on Thursday.

- He's got French on Thursday and on Friday after technology.

- He's got science on Thursday, after French.

- Wednesday starts with a double lesson and finishes with PE.

- He's got two science lessons each week.

	Monday	Tuesday	Wednesday	Thursday	Friday
lesson 1					
lesson 2					
lesson 3					
lesson 4					

Look at Kieran's schoolbag. What day is it?

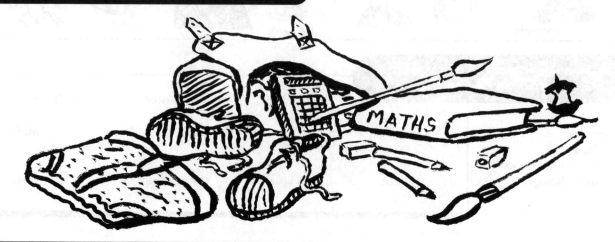

MATHS

Back to School!

Complete the crossword. What did Kevin forget to buy?

Make a list of the things that you need for school.
Are they the same as Kevin's things?

School Tour

You are visiting a new school.

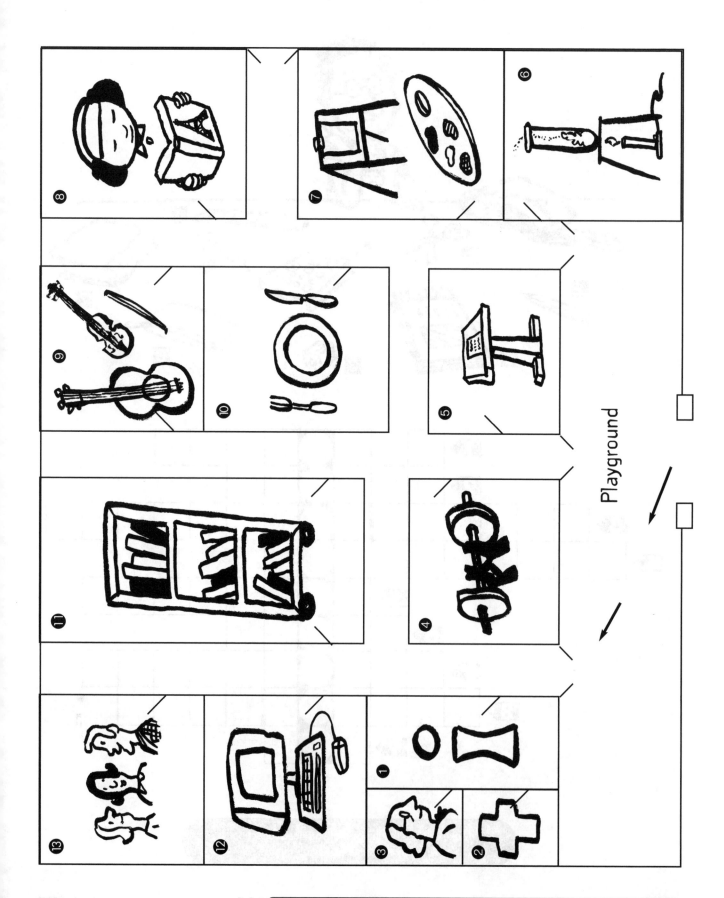

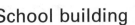 
Read the text and follow the guided tour. Draw the route.

Welcome to Cherwell High School. The tour starts in the **playground**. Here is the school **reception**, you can come here for help and information ... and this is the **medical room**, where we send you if you are hurt or ill. Now we come to **headteacher's office** – she's called Mrs Stone. This is the **staffroom**, where the teachers sit and rest. And this room here is the **computer room**. Now we cross the corridor to the **library**. Here you can borrow books and videos ... And this is the **gym**, where we do sports. Next to it, over here, is the **assembly hall**, where all the students meet every Monday morning. This is the **canteen**, where we have lunch. This is the **music room** and finally, opposite the music room is the **language laboratory**.

Now label the rooms that you saw on your tour.

1. reception _____
○ _____
○ _____
○ _____
○ _____
○ _____
○ _____
○ _____
○ _____
○ _____
○ _____
○ _____

Do you know the names of the rooms that you didn't visit?

○ _____
○ _____

Football Facts

How much do you know about football?
Read the sentences and choose the correct answers.

1. Who blows the whistle at the start of a match?
the referee D ...
the linesman M ...

2. What is the 15-minute break in the middle of the game?
half-time A ...
extra-time I ...

3. If a player commits a foul, he/she gets
a goal C ...
a yellow card V ...

4. If the score is 0–0, it's called
a draw I ...
a shoot-out H ...

5. When a player moves the ball with his/her head, it's called
a header D ...
a tackle A ...

6. Football rules are
different in each country W ...
international B ...

7. In a team, there are
11 players and 4 substitutes E ...
9 players and 6 substitutes L ...

8. Football was invented
in England C ...
in France O ...

9. The first footballs were made of
plastic L ...
leather K ...

10. A football match for under-13s lasts
70 minutes H ...
90 minutes O ...

11. Goalkeepers wear
shinpads A ...
helmets S ...

12. A football top is called
a blouse T ...
a shirt M ...

Ask your teacher for the answers.

What's your score?

Correct answers:

0–4
You aren't a football expert.

5–8
You're a keen football supporter.

9–12
You're football crazy!

Write the letters of the correct answers to spell the name of a famous English footballer.

The famous English footballer is

D _ _ _ _   _ _ _ _ _ _ _

Cine-madness!

Match the conversations to the people.

a. Excuse me, where are the toilets?   *In the foyer, next to the box office.*
b. I'd like some popcorn, please.   *Regular or large?*
c. Which screen is it for Star Wars?   *Screen number 2.*
d. One seat for Star Wars, please.   *I'm sorry, it's sold out.*
e. Mum, can we watch Blood Monster?   *No, it's a certificate 18.*

In the Department Store

What is everyone saying? Find the correct words for each person.

a. ~~Can I help you?~~

b. Do you sell football boots?

c. How much is the black one?

d. Can I try this on, please?

e. The changing room is over there, on the left.

f. It's too big.

g. It's too small.

h. It's too expensive.

i. Can I pay by credit card?

j. Keep the receipt in case you want to change it.

**Write a shopping dialogue.
Use some of the expressions above.**

Find it!

Tick the things that are in the picture.

1. ☑ steps
2. ☐ a door
3. ☐ a clock
4. ☐ a window
5. ☐ a chair
6. ☐ goggles
7. ☐ a whistle
8. ☐ insects
9. ☐ armbands
10. ☐ a lifeguard
11. ☐ showers
12. ☐ a swimming cap
13. ☐ a boat
14. ☐ a swimsuit
15. ☐ a fish
16. ☐ sand
17. ☐ a pair of sunglasses
18. ☐ a ball
19. ☐ a bag
20. ☐ a diving board
21. ☐ a duck

What's this?

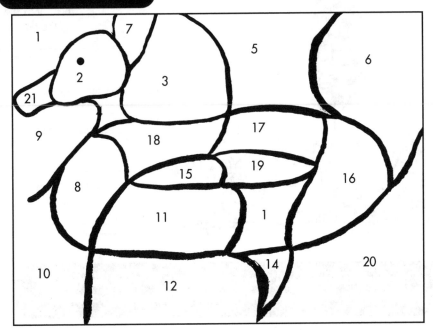

Colour the numbers that you ticked.
Find one of the things on the list above.

It's a _ _ _ _

Exploring Nature

Leo is visiting the countryside.
Circle the ten useful objects hidden in the picture.

| binoculars camera compass flask lighter |
| magnifying glass money belt penknife sunglasses torch |

Write each object that Leo is talking about.

I need them
to see far away.
1. *binoculars*

I need it to take photos.
6. _____

I need it to tell north from
south.
2. _____

I need them when
it's sunny.
7. _____

I need it to cut things.
3. _____

I need it to see
in the dark.
8. _____

I need it to light fires.
4. _____

I need it to keep my money
in.
9. _____

I need it to see
small things.
5. _____

I need it to keep my
water in.
10. _____

Make a list of the objects that you want for a visit to the countryside.
Have you got the same things as Leo? In pairs, compare your lists.

Translate!

Can you understand American English?
Find the English equivalents for these American words.

Now match the words to the pictures.

Example:
fall (The season before winter.)

| a d g |
| u t u |
| n m |

autumn - - - - - - - - - -

a) [10]

1. check
(You pay it in a restaurant.)

| b i x |
| o l e |
| a l t |

- - - - - - - - - - -

b) ☐

2. gas
(You put it in your car.)

| p t r |
| e o e |
| h l y |

- - - - - - - - - -

c) ☐

3. pants
(You wear them.)

| t r o |
| s i u |
| r e s |

- - - - - - - - - -

d) ☐

4. vacation
(Time to relax.)

| h a y |
| o d b |
| l i k |

- - - - - - - - - -

e) ☐

5. sidewalk
(You walk on it.)

| p v e |
| c a m |
| t n e |

- - - - - - - - - -

f)    ☐

ODEON
DINOSAUR
times: 4 o'clock
6 o'clock
8 o'clock

6. cookie
(You eat it as a snack.)

| b d e |
| s i t |
| c u i |

- - - - - - - - - -

7. trashcan
(You put your rubbish in it.)

| d u s |
| i b t |
| f n z |

- - - - - - - - - -

g) ☐

8. movies
(You see them at the cinema.)

| f a r |
| s i t |
| m l w |

- - - - - - - - - -

h) ☐

9. candy
(You eat these sugary things.)

| s g i |
| w e e |
| p s t |

- - - - - - - - - -

i) ☐

10. drapes
(They hang on the window.)

| c r h |
| s u t |
| n i a |

- - - - - - - - - -

j)  ☐

Spot the Country!

Find the second half of each label to show where the passengers are going.

Write the names of the countries below.

＿ ＿

＿ ＿

＿ ＿

＿ ＿ ＿ ＿ ＿ ＿ ＿ ＿ ＿

What's the weather like?

Colour the weather words. What is the weather man saying?

Today it's _____

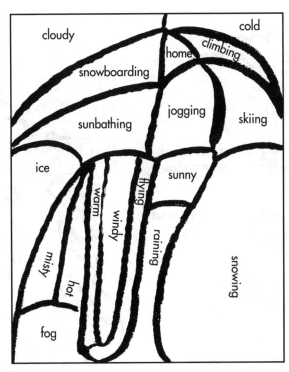

cloudy
cold
climbing
home
snowboarding
jogging
skiing
sunbathing
ice
sunny
warm
flying
windy
raining
misty
hot
snowing
fog

Look at the pictures and complete the sentences. Use the words in the box.

cloudy   cold   grey   raining   snowing
~~sunny~~   windy   rainbow

1 Today it's **sunny** but it's also _____
Jack is looking at a _____.

3 Today it's fine and it's very _____
Peter is flying his kite.

2 Today it's very _____
It's _____.

4 It's _____ and the sky is _____
Mrs Jones has got an umbrella.

Holiday Weather

Look at the map and read the postcards. Where are these people on holiday?

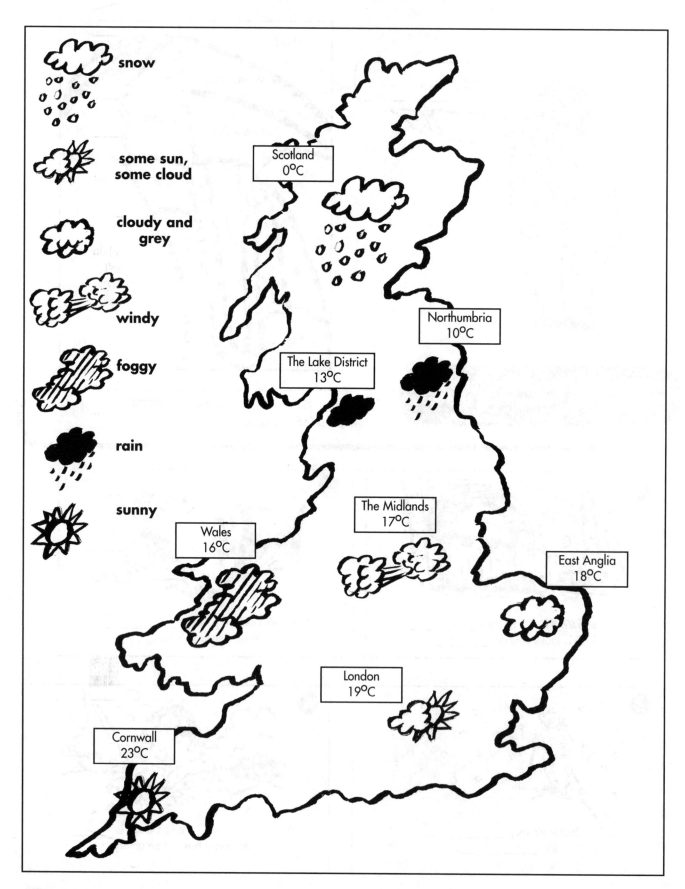

Dear Mum and Dad
It's very cold here in the mountains – there's a lot of snow. I go skiing every day!

Love from
Kevin

Dear Hannah
I'm enjoying my holiday. It's quite sunny, but not too hot. I'm taking a lot of photos!
See you next week.
Love
Richard

1. Richard is in ....

Kevin is in *Scotland*
....

3. Jason is in ....

Dear Grandma
The weather is awful! Today it's raining and the sky is cloudy. Where's the sun?!

Love
Anya

Dear Mum
It's dry today, but it's quite cloudy and cool. The sun isn't shining. We're going to ride our bikes later.

Love
Jason

Hi everybody
We're having a great holiday here, but the weather isn't very good. In the mornings, it's always misty and foggy.
Oh, well!
See you soon!
Lisa

2. Anya is in ....

5. Holly is in ....

4. Lisa is in ....

Dear Sam
It's a fine day – bright and very sunny. It's really hot, so we're going to the beach this afternoon.

Love
Holly

Dear Shana
It's a cloudy, grey day today and it's quite cold. We're going to the cinema this afternoon. Brr!

Love from Anil

6. Anil is in ....

Dear Andrew and Stuart
It's a fine day today, but very windy – a good day for flying a kite!

Love from
Grandpa

Write a postcard. What is the weather like today?

7. Grandpa is in ....

Crossword

Do the crossword.

Across

1   You can watch a play here.

2   You can find the mayor here (2 words).

3   Tourists sleep here.

4   If you need information about the town, go to the ___ office.

5   If you are lost, look at a ___ to find out where you are.

6   You can go here on Sunday to pray.

7   You can arrive at the town at the ___ station.

8   This building is like a large church.

9   You go to a restaurant to ___.

10 You go here to buy stamps.

11 You can go to the open-air swimming pool when the weather is ___.

12 The bus or train terminates here.

13 There is a lot of money here.

14 To report a crime, go to the ___ station.

Down

15 You can have lunch or dinner here.

16 There are lots of these at the campsite.

17 You can catch a ___ at a bus stop.

18 A bridge goes over it.

19 If you lose your umbrella, go to the ___ property office.

20 You can buy fresh vegetables and meat here.

21 You can go here to relax or do a sport.

22 The ___ of the hotel is 1, Beach Street.

23 You can put up your tent here.

24 If you are ___, you are not far away.

25 Nurses and doctors work here.

26 You can sit ___ a bench in the park.

27 What's the address — the hotel?

28 If you want to watch a film, go to the ___.

29 You can buy things here.

Crossword

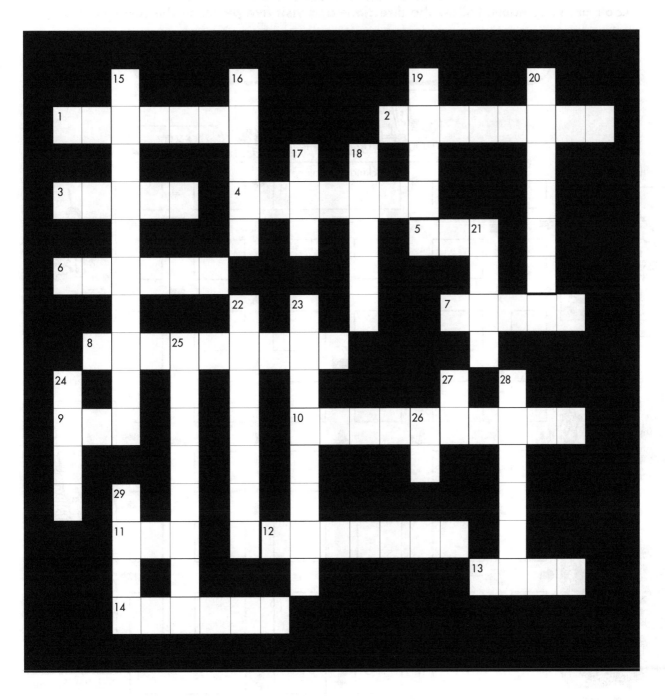

A Day Out in London

**There are a lot of things to see and do in London.
Look at the symbols. Follow the directions and visit five places in the correct order.**

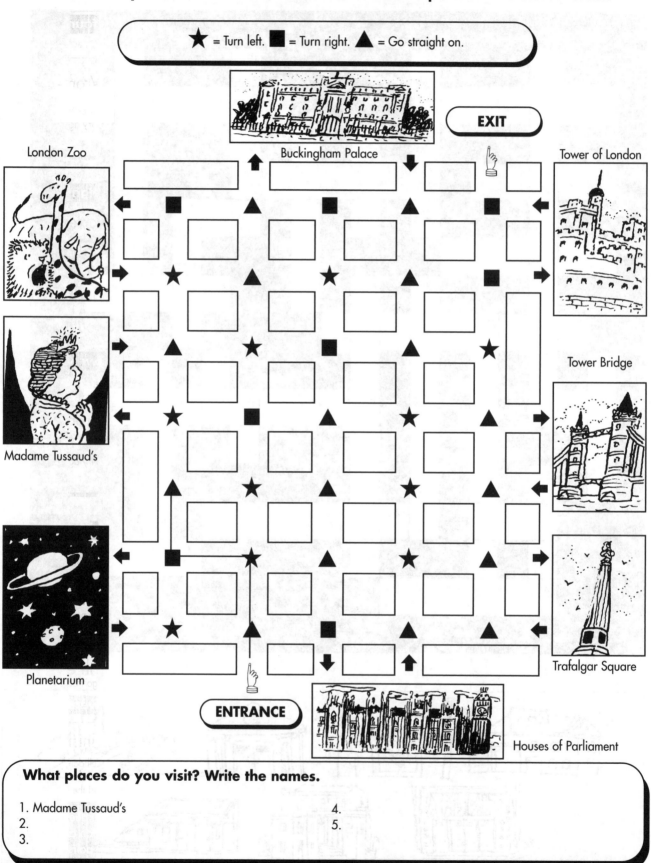

★ = Turn left. ■ = Turn right. ▲ = Go straight on.

EXIT

London Zoo
Buckingham Palace
Tower of London
Madame Tussaud's
Tower Bridge
Planetarium
Trafalgar Square
ENTRANCE
Houses of Parliament

What places do you visit? Write the names.

1. Madame Tussaud's   4.
2.   5.
3.

USA Quiz

The USA is the fourth largest country in the world. Can you find your way around it?

Do the quiz with a friend. Take turns to ask the questions. Start at number one.

one	two	three	four
Niagara Falls are on the USA–Canada border. Is that in the north or the south of the USA? **north** (go to 6) **south** (go to 15)	Wrong. Go back to 14 and try again.	Correct. Go to 20.	Wrong. Go back to 11 and try again.

five	six	seven	eight
Wrong. Go back to 16 and try again.	Correct. Disneyworld is in Florida, the Sunshine State. Is Florida in the south-east or the north-west of the USA? **south-east** (go to 19) **north-west** (go to 13)	Wrong. Go back to 9 and try again.	Correct. The largest state in the USA is Alaska, a land of mountains and glaciers. Is Akaska in the north or the south of the USA? **north** (go to 14) **south** (go to 18)

nine	ten	eleven	twelve
Correct. The Empire State Building is in New York City. Is New York on the east or the west coast of the USA? **east** (go to 16) **west** (go to 7)	Wrong. Go back to 19 and try again.	Correct. The islands of Hawaii are part of the USA. Is Hawaii to the south or to the west of the USA? **south** (go to 4) **west** (go to 17)	Wrong. Go back to 17 and try again.

thirteen	fourteen	fifteen	sixteen
Wrong. Go back to 6 and try again.	Correct. Hollywood, in California, is the centre of the film industry in the USA. Is Hollywood in the east or the west of the USA? **east** (go to 2) **west** (go to 11)	Wrong. Go back to 1 and try again.	Correct. In 1620, the first English colonists landed at Plymouth Rock, in Massachusetts. Is Massachusetts in the south-east or the north-east of USA? **south-east** (go to 5) **north-east** (go to 3)

seventeen	eighteen	nineteen	twenty
Correct. The state of Texas is famous for its oil, cotton and cattle. Is Texas in the south or the north of the USA? **south** (go to 9) **north** (go to 12)	Wrong. Go back to 8 and try again.	Correct. Washington DC is the capital of the USA. Is Washington DC in the east or the west of the USA? **east** (go to 8) **west** (go to 10)	Finish Well done! Now you can find your way around the USA.

Invent questions about the location of places in your country. In pairs, ask and answer your questions.

Picture Crossword

Complete the crossword.

Down

1

3

5

7

9

11

Across

2

4

6

8

10

12

Look at the forms of transport again and answer the questions.
Discuss your answers with a partner.

1   Which form of transport is the fastest?
2   Which is the slowest?
3   Which is the most comfortable?
4   Which is the most exciting?
5   Which is the smallest?
6   Which can travel the longest distance without stopping?

Transport Puzzle

What is the mystery form of transport?
Are the sentences true or false? Follow the arrows.
The letters spell the name of a form of transport.

→	**True**
⇢	**False**

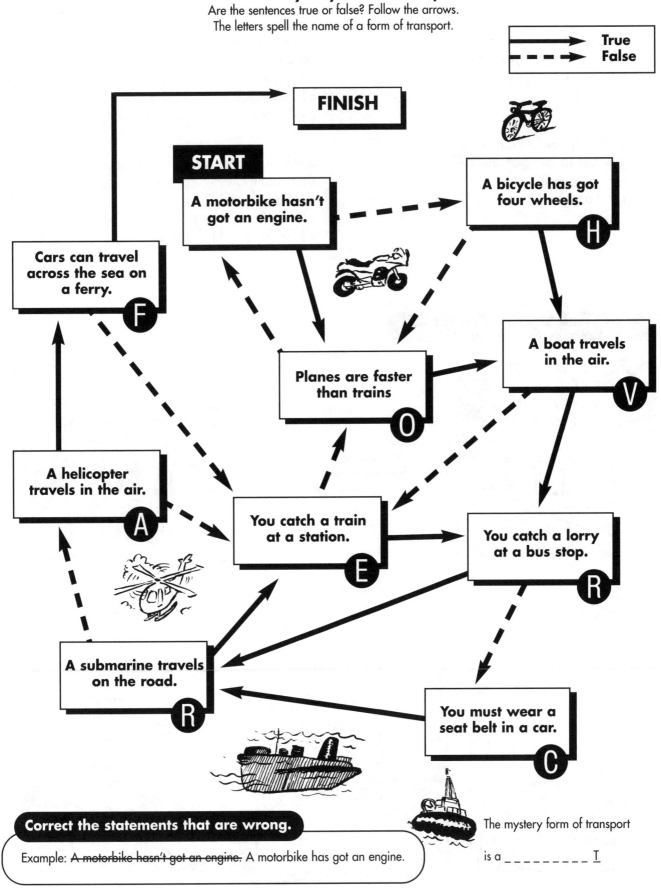

FINISH

START

A motorbike hasn't got an engine.

A bicycle has got four wheels. **H**

Cars can travel across the sea on a ferry. **F**

Planes are faster than trains **O**

A boat travels in the air. **V**

A helicopter travels in the air. **A**

You catch a train at a station. **E**

You catch a lorry at a bus stop. **R**

A submarine travels on the road. **R**

You must wear a seat belt in a car. **C**

Correct the statements that are wrong.

Example: A motorbike hasn't got an engine. A motorbike has got an engine.

The mystery form of transport
is a _ _ _ _ _ _ _ _ _ T

Transport Quiz

Choose the correct answers.

1. Which type of transport can you **get on** and **get off**?

a [ ] a car
b [ ] a train

2. Which type of transport can you **get in** and **get out of**?

a [ ] a motorbike
b [ ] a taxi

3 Which of these types of transport do you **catch**? There are four correct answers.

a [ ] a train   b [ ] a plane
c [ ] a bicycle   d [ ] a bus
e [ ] a car   f [ ] the underground

4 Which of these types of transport do you **ride**? There are two correct answers.

a [ ] a ferry   b [ ] a scooter
c [ ] a coach   d [ ] a car
e [ ] a lorry   f [ ] a bicycle

Match the sentences with the pictures.

1 Fasten your seatbelts – we're landing in five minutes.

2 Welcome aboard! We sail from Portsmouth Harbour in five minutes.

3 We're taking off! Here we go!

4 Which stop do you want to get off at?

5 Hyde Park? Get in! It's just around the corner.

At the Railway Station

What are the people saying?
Match the sentences to the people.

1. Which platform is the train to Glasgow?	e	6. Single or return?		
2. Is this platform 11?		7. Here's a timetable.		
3. Where is the left luggage office?		8. Look on the screens.		
4. A ticket to London, please.		9. It's next to the waiting room.		
5. How long is the journey from London to Dover?		10. No, this is platform 1.		

At the Airport

What can you see at the airport?
Look at the signs and write the words.

- ⑥ filts
- ⑨ felt glugage
- ⑧ salvarri
- ③ ottiles
- ④ paretured tsage
- ① regfoni crurncey
- ⑤ kecch-in
- ② minifoatron
- ⑦ pratspos cronlot

1. F O R E I G N C U R R E N C Y
2. I ☐ ☐ ☐ ⦿ ☐ ☐ ☐
3. T ☐ ☐ ☐ ☐ ⦿ ☐ ☐
4. D ☐ ☐ ☐ ☐ ☐ ☐ ☐ ☐ ☐ ☐ ⦿ ☐
5. C ☐ ☐ ☐ ☐ – ☐ ⦿
6. L ⦿ ☐ ☐ ☐
7. P ☐ ☐ ⦿ ☐ ☐ ☐ ☐ ☐ ☐ ☐ ☐ ☐ ☐
8. A ☐ ☐ ☐ ☐ ⦿ ☐ ☐
9. L ☐ ☐ ☐ ☐ ☐ ☐ ☐ ⦿ ☐

Now write the letters from inside the circles. What is the passenger saying?

$\overline{}_{6}$ $\overline{}_{2}$ $\overline{}_{6}$ $\overline{}_{3}$ $\overline{}_{3}$ $\overline{}_{4}$ D

$\overline{}_{2}$ $\overline{}_{1}$ $\overline{}_{7}$ $\overline{}_{8}$ $\overline{}_{9}$ $\overline{}_{5}$ $\overline{}_{4}$!

Orienteering

These climbers have to reach one of the meeting points (A, B, or C) in the mountains.

Read the instructions and trace the route on the map. Which meeting point are they going to?

> Go to the Start. Go through the forest.
> Go round the forest and past the waterfall.
> Cross at the third bridge.
> Follow the track past the wooden hut.
> Go up the rocky slope up to the peak.
> Go down past the caves. Keep the caves on your right!
> The meeting point is at the start of the footpath
> down to the ski resort at the bottom of the valley.

Write instructions to get to a different meeting point.
Read the instructions to your partner. Can your partner find the meeting point?

What can you see?

Tick the things that are in the picture.

1.	some birds	☐	I
2.	a barn	☐	S
3.	a field	☐	C
4.	a river	☐	A
5.	a church	☐	P
6.	a farmhouse	☐	R
7.	a road	☐	E
8.	a hill	☐	C
9.	a wood	☐	R
10.	a fox	☐	O
11.	a tractor	☐	W
12.	some flowers	☐	H
13.	some sheep	☐	N
14.	a horse	☐	T
15.	some cows	☐	B

What is standing in the middle of the field?
Write the letters that you ticked above.

There's a <u>S</u> _ _ _ _ _ _ _ _ in the middle of the field.

**Now look at the words that you didn't tick.
Draw these things in the picture.**

Which inventions?

Match the two halves of each word to find six inventions.

fire   work
lawn   net
skate   mower
inter   craft
hover   washer
dish   board

a)

_____

b)

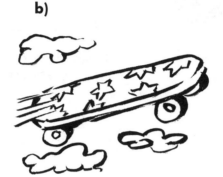

_____

c)

_____

d)

_____

e)

_____

f)

_____

**Now read the descriptions.
Write the names of the inventions.**

1. You cut the grass with a lawn mower.

2. You can travel on water and land in a _____.

3. A _____ washes the dishes for you.

4. You stand on a _____ and it moves on its wheels.

5. You search the _____ with a computer.

6. A _____ explodes in the sky with a bang and colours.

Guess the inventions!

Student A

Now show your partner the pictures of the inventions.

 1

You use this hot metal object on your clothes.

2

You use this to tidy your hair.

3

You use this to keep you dry in the rain.

4

The machine sends words and pictures.

5

This wakes you up in the morning.

Listen to your partner's description of the inventions. Can you guess what they are? Use the words in the box.

mobile phone
pencil case
razor
towel
vacuum cleaner

Student B

Listen to your partner's description of the inventions. Can you guess what they are? Use the words in the box.

comb
alarm clock
fax machine
iron
umbrella

Read the descriptions of the inventions to your partner. Can your partner guess what the inventions are?

1

You dry yourself with this.

2

Men use this to shave their beards.

3

You can use this type of telephone anywhere!

4

This machine cleans the house.

5

You keep your pens and pencils in this.

Now show your partner the pictures of the inventions.

Environmental Quiz

How much do you know about protecting the environment? Read these facts about protecting the environment and decide which are true and which are false.

Circle your answer and put the letter at the end in the box. The letters will spell the name of an organisation concerned with protecting the environment.

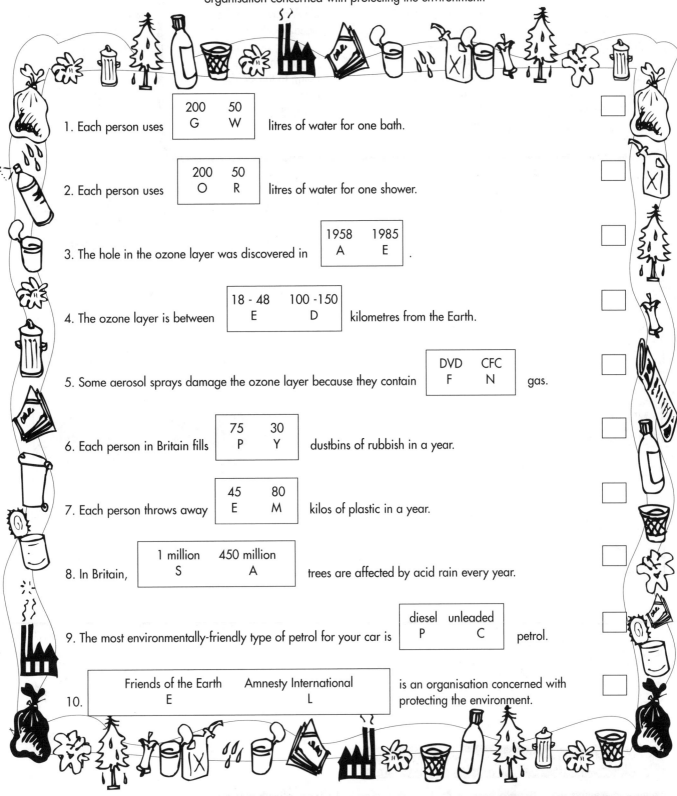

1. Each person uses | 200   50 / G   W | litres of water for one bath.

2. Each person uses | 200   50 / O   R | litres of water for one shower.

3. The hole in the ozone layer was discovered in | 1958   1985 / A   E | .

4. The ozone layer is between | 18 - 48   100 -150 / E   D | kilometres from the Earth.

5. Some aerosol sprays damage the ozone layer because they contain | DVD   CFC / F   N | gas.

6. Each person in Britain fills | 75   30 / P   Y | dustbins of rubbish in a year.

7. Each person throws away | 45   80 / E   M | kilos of plastic in a year.

8. In Britain, | 1 million   450 million / S   A | trees are affected by acid rain every year.

9. The most environmentally-friendly type of petrol for your car is | diesel   unleaded / P   C | petrol.

10. | Friends of the Earth   Amnesty International / E   L | is an organisation concerned with protecting the environment.

Make a poster to encourage people to protect the environment.

Hobbies A-Z

Can you find a hobby for every letter of the alphabet?
Write the hobby under the correct picture.

football	**b**allet	**w**eight-lifting
photography	**e**-mailing friends	playing the **x**ylophone
doing **q**uizzes	**k**nitting	**n**eedlework
playing the **g**uitar	playing **c**hess	watching **t**elevision
judo	**d**rawing	playing the **u**kelele
~~**a**rchery~~	listening to **m**usic	going to the **o**pera
horse-riding	**s**inging	**r**eading
zzzzz (sleeping!)	**l**earning a foreign	doing **y**oga
playing **v**ideo games	language	
surfing the **i**nternet		

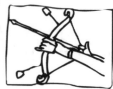

A

archery

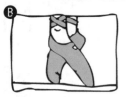
B
- - - - - - - - - -

C
- - - - - - - - - -

D
- - - - - - - - - -

E
- - - - - - - - - -

... (F)

G

H

I

J

K

L

M

N

O

P

Q

R

S

T

U

V

W

X

Y

Z

Which hobby in the list do you think is ...

the most interesting _____?
the most boring _____?
the most exciting_____?

the most difficult to learn _____?
the most expensive _____?
the most relaxing _____?

Summer Camp

**Someone has rubbed all the vowels 'a, e , i, o, u' off the poster.
Write them back in to see the activities you can do at the camp.**

Come to camp this summer!

Here are some of the activities you can try ...

s u rf i ng

c_n _ _ _ ng

w_nds_rf_ng

d _ nc _ ng

f _ _ tb _ ll

r _ ck-cl_ mb_ng

f _ sh _ ng

i_d_

v _ ll _ yb _ ll

q _ _ zz _ s

dr _ m _

w _ tch _ ng
v_ d _ _ s

k _ r _ _ k _

Two activities are not pictured on the poster. Which?

1. ....

2. ....

If you went to the camp, which activities
would you like to try? Choose four
from the list.

What's Your Ideal Holiday?

Do the quiz. Circle your answers.

1. You have nothing to do one sunny afternoon, so ...

★ you ask a friend to play a game of tennis.
▼ you go sunbathing.
✪ you start reading a new book.

2. Your best friend comes to your house, so ...

★ you go for a walk.
▼ you watch television.
✪ you play table tennis.

3. You are on your own at home, so ...

★ you play with a ball in the garden.
▼ you wash your hair.
✪ you surf the internet.

4. You have to make a holiday lunch for your little brother and sister, so ...

★ you cycle to a forest and have a picnic.
▼ you order some takeaways.
✪ you cook a chinese meal.

5. For your holiday, you can only pack important things in your backpack, so ...

★ you take your swimming costume and snorkel so you can go swimming.
▼ you take your CD player and some CDs so you can listen to music.
✪ you take a pair of binoculars so you can go bird-watching.

6. What is your worst type of holiday?

★ doing nothing and being bored.
▼ rock climbing, canoeing, playing volleyball.
✪ doing the same thing every day.

7. Which school trip would you choose?

★ Skiing in the mountains.
▼ Sunbathing at the beach.
✪ Sightseeing in London.

Count your symbols. How many have you got? Read the results.

Mostly ✪: You like to discover new things. Choose a holiday where you can visit new places.

Mostly ▼: You hate too much sport and activity. Choose a holiday where you can relax and be lazy.

Mostly ★: You love sport and activity. Choose a holiday where you can be active and make friends.

Spot the Sport!

Write the names of sports under the pictures. What is missing from each picture?

1. _ _ _ [_] _ _ _ _ _

2. _ [_] _ _ _ _ _

3. [_] _ _ _ _

4. _ _ _ [_] _ _ _ _

5. _ _ _ _ [_] _ _ _ _

6. _ [_] _ _ _ _

7. _ _ [_] _ _ _

8. _ _ [_] _

9. _ _ _ _ [_] _

10. _ _ _ _ _ _ [_] _

11. [_] _ _ _

Discover the mystery sport with the letters in brackets. What's missing from the picture?

Mystery sport

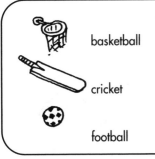

_____

 basketball

 golf

judo

 swimming

cricket

ice hockey

rugby

 tennis

football

ice skating

 skiing

What sports do you like?

Sports Collocations

Look at the list of sports, activities and leisure interests.
We use different verbs with different sports. Put the sports with the correct verb.

~~aerobics~~	hockey	skiing	taekwondo
baseball	horse-riding	snooker	volleyball
gymnastics	jogging	table tennis	yoga

aerobics

do

go

play

Can you think of any more sports, activities and leisure interests for each group?

What are you watching?

Cross out the letters making up the title of each programme.
The letters remaining spell out what kind of programmes they are.
Write them under the televisions.

Sky 1

Ꝉøcakrøtomønon

1. _cartoon_ _____

BBC Choice

Tcheilledren'stumsshow

2. _____

ITV

Ninghetlwynesws

3. _____

Sky moviemax

Tfitainilmc

4. _____

Discovery

Wdoilcudlimenftarey

5. _____

Channel 4

Flasetrimaestes

6. _____

BBC 2

Mspoartchtsproofgrathemdamey

7. _____

Channel 5

O,taplkrshaow

8. _____

UK Gold

Gacomeunsthuopw

9. _____

What are your favourite television programmes?

Crazy Party!

Something's wrong! Find the correct bubble for each person!

1. Where's the toilet?

2. Oh, yes, please!

3. Have some cake!

4. Upstairs on the left.

5. This is my friend, Ellie.

6. Yes, I am. Great party!

7. Sorry I'm late!

8. Are you enjoying yourself?

9. Nice to meet you.

10. Please come in.

A	B	C	D	E	F	G	H	I	J
7									

Musical Instruments

Unscramble the names of the musical instruments and write them in the grid.

1. olivin

2. creedror

3. lolce

4. raph

5. tulfe

6. smurd

7. prumtet

8. treclain

9. anpoi

**Use the letters in the circles
to find the answer to this question.**

Where can you find all these instruments together?

In an _____

In the Pet Shop

Can you match the words and pictures of the pets?

parrot   snake   rabbit
kitten   hamster   canary
puppy   guinea pig   goldfish
        tortoise

**Read the descriptions of the pets below their homes.
Then write the name of each pet in the correct homes.**

tortoise

1. I live in my shell. Touch it, and
I'll go inside it!

2. I am long and thin, with scales
on my shiny skin.

3. I like eating lettuce and carrots.
Stroke my long ears!

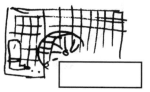

4. I am small and gold and furry, with
tiny pink ears.

5. I am black and white and cuddly. You
can't really see my ears!

6. I like talking! Look at my bright
colours and big beak!

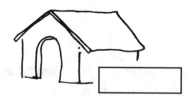

7. I like digging in the garden. Listen to
my bark!

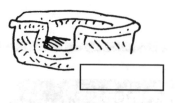

8. I like drinking milk.
Feel my soft fur.

9. I can sing beautifully. Look at my
lovely yellow feathers.

10. I am orange and I've got a tail.
I don't make a noise.

Which of these pets would you like?
Which wouldn't you like? Why?

Pairs

Match the pieces of paper to find 13 farm animals.

Write the name of the animal under the correct picture.

1. _horse_

2. _ _ _ _ _ _ _ _ _ _ _

3. _ _ _ _ _ _ _ _ _ _ _

4. _ _ _ _ _ _ _ _ _ _ _

5. _ _ _ _ _ _ _ _ _ _ _

6. _ _ _ _ _ _ _ _ _ _ _

7. _ _ _ _ _ _ _ _ _ _ _

8. _ _ _ _ _ _ _ _ _ _ _

9. _ _ _ _ _ _ _ _ _ _ _

10. _ _ _ _ _ _ _ _ _ _ _

11. _ _ _ _ _ _ _ _ _ _ _

12. _ _ _ _ _ _ _ _ _ _ _

13. _ _ _ _ _ _ _ _ _ _ _

Anna's Diary

Anna is on safari. She passes lots of animals. Read her diary. Draw in her route.

Where does she stop for the night (A, B, C or D)?

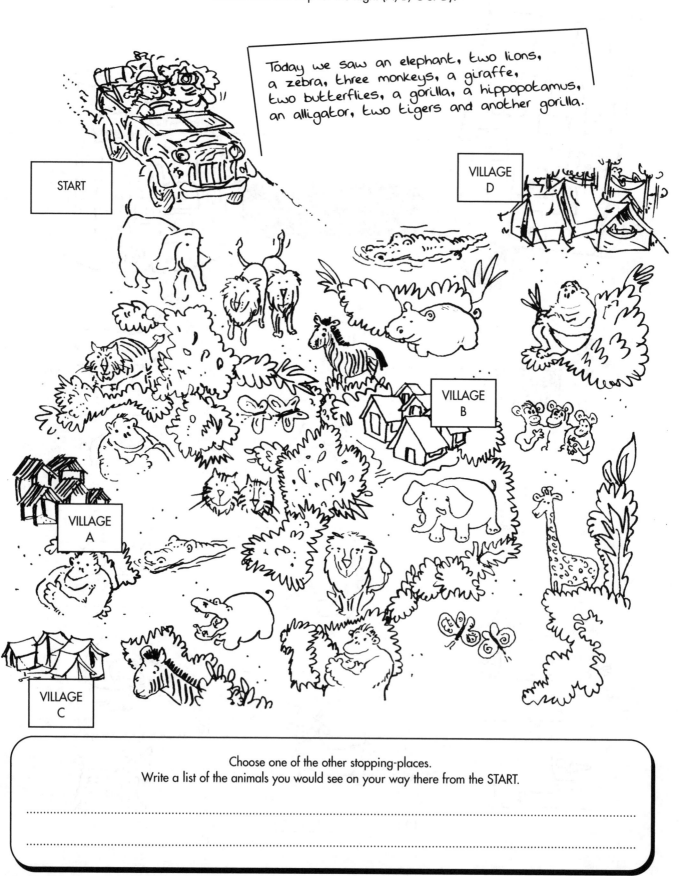

Today we saw an elephant, two lions, a zebra, three monkeys, a giraffe, two butterflies, a gorilla, a hippopotamus, an alligator, two tigers and another gorilla.

START

VILLAGE D

VILLAGE B

VILLAGE A

VILLAGE C

Choose one of the other stopping-places.
Write a list of the animals you would see on your way there from the START.

....

....

Animal Facts

What animal was most sacred to the ancient Egyptians?
To find out, read the sentences and choose TRUE or FALSE, then join the dots.
Example: If you think sentence 1 is true, join 2 and 50.
If you think it is false, join 2 and 27.
Use the internet to find out the facts.

		TRUE	FALSE
1.	The tallest animal is the giraffe.	2 - 50	2 - 27
2.	The animal with the longest nose is the dog.	27 - 50	27 - 5
3.	The largest animal is the blue whale.	5 - 16	5 - 13
4.	The fastest animal is the horse.	44 - 50	44 - 33
5.	The bird that is best at talking is the parrot.	39 - 3	39 - 16
6.	The most ferocious fish is the piranha.	46 - 50	46 - 31
7.	The largest bird's egg is laid by the eagle.	12 - 3	12 - 2
8.	The longest snake is the python.	13 - 27	13 - 50
9.	The loudest insect is the cicada.	36 - 46	31 - 13
10.	The fussiest eater is the rabbit.	16 - 18	16 - 44
11.	A hamster has eight eyes.	12 - 50	12 - 13
12.	The most destructive insect is the bee.	33 - 46	33 - 45
13.	The biggest lizard is the male komodo dragon.	10 - 36	10 - 12
14.	The largest member of the cat family is the wild cat.	3 - 27	3 - 45

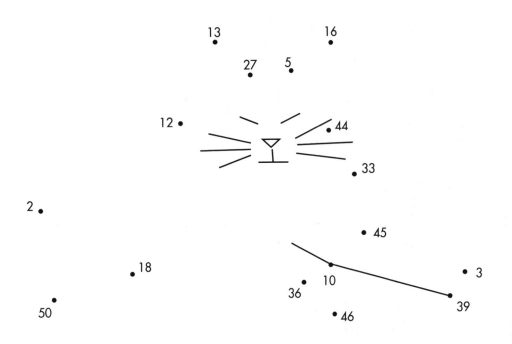

The .... was the most sacred animal to the ancient Egyptians.

Christmas Cards

Find the following objects on the Christmas cards.
Write the correct number next to each word.

angel	_ _	Christmas carol	_ _	decorations	_ _	reindeer	_ _
bell	_ _	Christmas pudding	_ _	Father Christmas	_ _	roast turkey	_ _
card	_ _	Christmas tree	_ _	mince pies	_ _	snow	_ _
chimney	_ _	cracker	_ _	mistletoe	_ _	star	_ _
Christmas cake	_ _	crib	_ _	present	_ _	three kings	_ _

Now join the dots in the same order as the list above. What object appears on the last Christmas card?

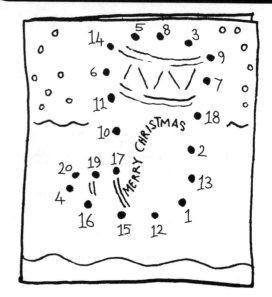

Christmas Presents

Help Father Christmas! Write what each present is.

> trainers CD sports bag video perfume computer game
> board game necklace football chocolates book jumper

⑧ n _ _ _ _ _ _ _

① <u>t r a i n e r s</u>

⑩ C _

⑥ c _ _ _ _ _ _ _ _

③ c _ _ _ _ _ _ _

⑨ b _ _ _ _ _ _

⑦ b _ _ _

⑤ p _ _ _ _ _ _

② v _ _ _ _

④ f _ _ _ _ _ _ _

⑪ j _ _ _ _ _

⑫ s _ _ _ _ _ _ _ _ _

Now write the correct name on each label.

• Lucy loves jewellery.
• Nick is crazy about all sports.
• Jane likes designer clothes and shoes.
• Paul likes listening to music.
• Mike likes playing games.
• Emma likes new clothes.
• Julia reads a lot.

• Toby likes films.
• Rob loves football.
• Sylvie likes to smell nice.
• Chris loves chocolate.
• Mark's mad about computers.

What are you going to give your family and friends for Christmas? Write a list.

Greetings!

Send each card on the right day! Match each card with the correct greeting.

 A

 B

 C

 D

 E

 F

1. Happy Birthday! ☐

2. Happy Mother's Day! ☐

3. Merry Christmas and Happy New Year! **A**

4. Congratulations! ☐

5. Good luck! ☐

6. Happy Valentine's Day! ☐

Write the greeting on each of these cards.

❶

❸

❷

❹

Holiday Souvenirs

Match the words to find the souvenirs.
Write them below the pictures.

beach

teddy

post

bear

case

shirt

flip

sun

book

hat

tea

card

straw

swim

mug

towel

pencil

glasses

bag

coffee

T-

magnet

flops

neck

fridge

guide

lace

suit

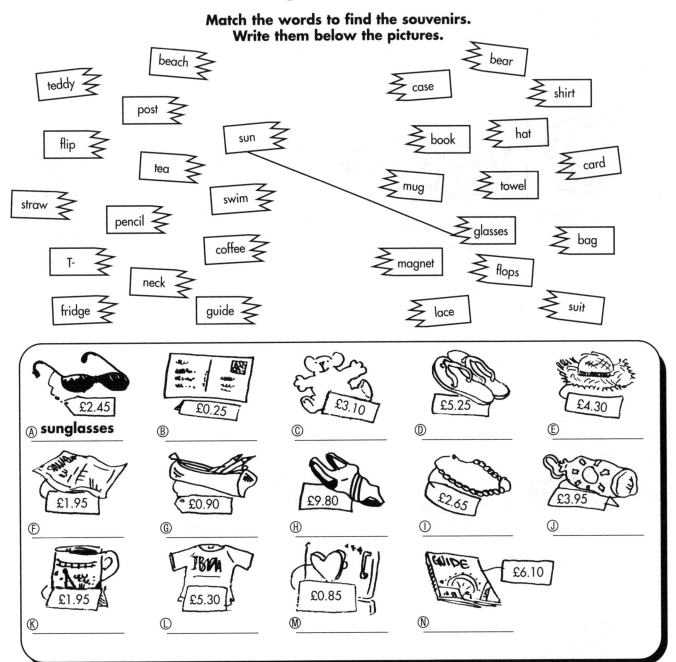

Ⓐ **sunglasses** £2.45

Ⓑ £0.25

Ⓒ £3.10

Ⓓ £5.25

Ⓔ £4.30

Ⓕ £1.95

Ⓖ £0.90

Ⓗ £9.80

Ⓘ £2.65

Ⓙ £3.95

Ⓚ £1.95

Ⓛ £5.30

Ⓜ £0.85

Ⓝ £6.10

How much has each holiday-maker spent?

1 _ _ _ _ _ _ _ _ _ _ _ _

2 _ _ _ _ _ _ _ _ _ _ _ _

3 _ _ _ _ _ _ _ _ _ _ _ _

Seaside Holiday

You need a die and a counter for each player. Follow the instructions. If they are no instructions, you must make a sentence with the picture. If you can't, you must go back one space. Good luck!

Throw a six to start your holiday. Then throw again.

1	2	3	4
 You love the sea! Throw again!	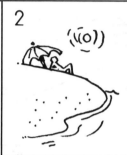	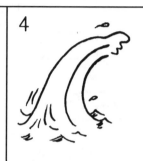 You've forgotten your swimsuit. Go back to START!	

20	19	18	17	16
 You don't want to go fishing. Go forward one space.		 You're going fishing. Go forward one space.		Your tent blows away! Go back to start.

21				

22	23	24	25	26
	 You're resting at the campsite. Go back one or two spaces.	 You're sunburnt. Go back to number 12.	 You enjoy beach volleyball. Throw again.	 You're hungry. Go to number 28.

Seaside Holiday

5

The sea is cold. Miss a turn.

6

7

You're looking for a campsite. Go forward two spaces.

8

The campsite is full. Find another. Miss a turn.

9

10

It's hot and sunny. Go forward three spaces.

15

There's a terrible storm. Go forward two spaces.

14

You fall off your windsurfer.

13

You enjoy windsurfing. Throw again!

12

11

You don't have any sun cream. Go back two places.

27

You're buying souvenirs. Miss a turn.

28

29

Say goodbye to your new friends. Go back to number 25.

30

Throw a six to go home.

Holiday Code

Match the holiday verbs and nouns and write the code.

1. do	C swimming	1. = G
2. take	V a bicycle	2. =
3. buy	U a sandcastle	3. =
4. hire	A photos	4. =
5. eat	B an ice-cream	5. =
6. visit	M a theme park	6. =
7. climb	N a mountain	7. =
8. board	G a bungy-jump	8. =
9. build	S souvenirs	9. =
10. make	T friends	10. =
11. watch	P the plane	11. =
12. send	O musical	12. =
13. pack	L a postcard	13. =
14. play	I your suitcase	14. =
15. go	E beach volleyball	15. =

Use the code to read the holiday postcard.

Where did Tom go on holiday? Choose the correct postcard.

2-7-7-2,

_____

13 12-11-4-14 15-12-13-6-5-13-7-1 6-11-9-7-10-2-13-7-3

_____

5-9-10 5-14-7 7-14-4-13-3 13-3 10-11-11 5-13-1! 13 2-6

_____

4-13-3-13-10-13-7-1 6-9-3-14-9-6-3. 13 12-11-4-14

_____

12-13-3-10-14-7-13-7-1 10-11 5-2-1-8-13-8-14 6-9-3-13-15.

_____

12-11-4-14 10-11-6

_____

Answers

PAGE 4 My family

Emily is saying,
'This is Andrew.
He's my **cousin**'.

PAGE 5 Family tree

1.

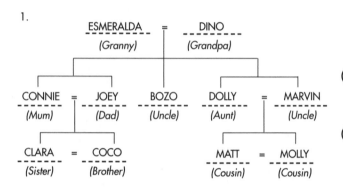

2. Molly is wrong. She's got **one** brother and two cousins.

PAGE 6 Football training

The referee is tall. He's got short, dark hair. He doesn't wear glasses.

PAGE 7 Wanted!

Students ask a maximum of ten questions to find which suspect their partner chose.

PAGE 8 The Monster

Students label the picture of the monster.
1. True.   2. False. He's got four ears.
3. True.   4. True.   5. False.

PAGE 9 Personality Spiral

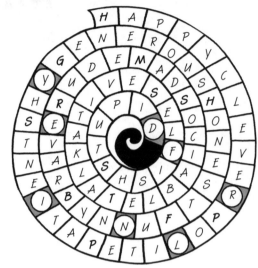

The alien is saying, 'I'm **friendly**'.
1. happy   2. generous 3. patient   4. brave   5. rude

PAGE 10 How sensitive are you?

Students complete the quiz and check their score.

PAGE 11 How old are you?

a. True.   b. True.   c. False.   d. True.   e. False.
f. True.   g. True.   h. False.   i. True.   j. True.
k. False.   l. True.   m. True.   n. True.   o. False.
p. True.
Lauren's cat is **10**.

PAGE 12 Inventions

1. A; 2. M; 3. E; 4. R; 5. I; 6. C; 7. A; 8. N
The first jukeboxes were **American**.

PAGE 13 Puzzle It Out

1. Simon   2. Carly   3. Anna   4. Robbie   5. Elena   6. Daniel
Luke feels **scared**

PAGE 14 Feeling ill

1. sore throat   2. cold   3. headache
4. toothache   5. stomach ache   6. earache
7. cut
The Doctor says, "**Go to bed!**"

PAGE 15 In My Opinion...

1. Fishing is boring 2. Fishing is relaxing 3. Parachuting is frightening
4. Parachuting is exciting 5. Shopping is irritating 6. Shopping is
great fun   7. Reading is interesting   8. Reading is OK

PAGES 16 & 17 Telling the Time

No answer – game

PAGES 18 & 19   Opening and Closing Times

	opening time	closing time
bank	9am	4pm
tourist office	9.30am	5.30pm
castle	11am	7.30pm
post office	9am	5pm
supermarket	8.30am	11pm
chemist's	8.30am	6pm
department store	9am	5pm
library	9am	8pm
museum	10.30am	6pm
cinema	2.30pm	11.30pm
bowling alley	3.30pm	11.30pm
swimming pool	7am	9.45pm
sports centre	7am	9.45pm
theme park	10.30am	8pm
zoo	10.30am	8.30pm
disco	7.30pm	2am

PAGE 20   Dates for your calendar

Ranjit's birthday 3rd August; Christmas Day 25th December;
Bonfire Night 5th November; Diwali October;
New Year's day 1st January; Valentine's Day 14th February;
Exams start 10th May; Summer holidays start 24th July;
Mother's Day March; Father's Day June

PAGE 21   Numbers Picture

3 monkeys   2 elephants   4 lions   12 birds
5 sea lions   8 clouds   7 dustbins   14 children
3 zoo-keepers 10 trees   15 butterflies

PAGE 22 & 23   Collection Crazy!

No answer – game

PAGE 24   On the Washing Line

1. shirt   2. T-shirt   3. sweatshirt   4. skirt
5. jeans   6. trousers   7. dress   8. socks
Kevin is wearing **trainers**.

PAGE 25   Hide and Seek

Peter and Sophie

PAGE 26   Eurocolours

a. Austria   b. Belgium   c. Denmark
d. Finland   e. France   f. Germany
g. Greece   h. Ireland   i. Italy
j. Luxembourg   k. Netherlands   l. Portugal
m. Spain   n. Sweden   o. United Kingdom

PAGE 27   Helping Out At Home

Students complete the quiz and check their score.

PAGE 28   Fruity Fun!

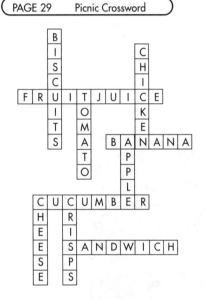

The worm's question is **Do you like strawberries?**

PAGE 29   Picnic Crossword

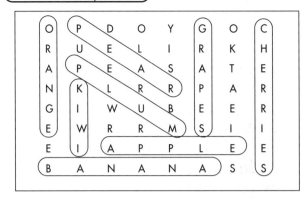

Nicky forgot **chocolate cake**.

PAGE 30   Which Shop?

A. BUTCHER'S   B. BAKER'S   C. CHEMIST'S
D. NEWSAGENT'S   E. PET SHOP   F. MUSIC SHOP
1. pet shop   2. newsagent's   3. chemist's
4. butcher's   5. music shop   6. baker's

PAGE 31   Health Quiz

1. a   2. h   3. g   4. e   5. i   6. b   7. j   8. c   9. d   10. f
Students complete the quiz and check their score.

PAGES 32 & 33   Choose a Job!

1. maths teacher   2. accountant   3. tour guide
4. translator   5. physiotherapist   6. sports teacher
7. editor   8. newspaper reporter 9. marine biologist
10. doctor   11. actor   12. film director
13. farmer   14. town planner

PAGE 34   Who lives where?

1. Jill   2. Michelle   3. Lisa   4. Oliver
5. Danielle   6. Joe   7. Mark   8. Adam
Sentence 3 (Lisa lives in a flat.) is wrong.

PAGE 35   Where's Harry the hamster?

Harry is behind the TV in the living room.

PAGES 36 & 37   In Lee's/Laura's Bedroom

Lee's present is a book. It's under the chair.
Laura's present is a teddy bear. It's on the wardrobe.

PAGE 38   Mystery Objects

1. a – cooker   2. b – tin opener
3. b – washing machine   4. c – saucepan
5. c – broom   6. a – kettle
Eight objects from exercise 1 are in the picture: a teapot; a tap;
a broom; a washing machine; a cooker; a kettle; a vacuum cleaner; a tin
opener.

PAGE 39   Picture Crossword

PAGE 40   Vampire Scare!

Picture A
1. cat   2. Grandpa   3. Grandma   4. Billy   5. fish   6. Bella

Picture **B**
fish   I'm **in** the fireplace.
cat   I'm **on** the table.
Bella   I'm **next to** the TV.
Billy   I'm **in front of** the curtains.
Grandma   I'm **behind** the sofa.
Grandpa   I'm **under** the armchair.

PAGE 41   Find the Bag

a. geography b. art   c. maths   d. technology
e. French   f. science   g. biology   h. IT
i. RE   j. English   k. PE   l. history

Suggested answers:
Mr Keyboard – IT   Ms Marathon – PE
Mr Globe – geography   Ms Portrait – art
Mr Numbers – maths   Ms Past – history
Mr Metal – technology   Ms Croissant – French
Ms X-ray – science   Mr Cambridge – English

PAGE 42   School Timetable

	Monday	Tuesday	Wednesday	Thursday	Friday
lesson 1	science	maths	art	maths	technology
lesson 2	IT	history	art	French	technology
lesson 3	PE	RE	maths	science	French
lesson 4	English	English	PE	history	English

Today it's **Wednesday**.

PAGE 43   Back to school

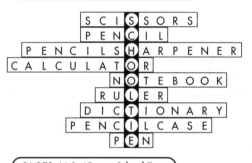

PAGES 44 & 45   School Tour

The rooms on the tour are:
1. reception   2. medical room   3. headteacher's office
13. staffroom 12. computer room 11. library   4. gym
5. assembly hall 10. canteen 9. music room 8. language laboratory

The rooms that the students don't visit are:
7. art room
6. science laboratory

PAGE 46   Football Facts

1. D   2. A   3. V   4. I   5. D
6. B   7. E   8. C   9. K   10. H
11. A   12. M
The famous English footballer is **David Beckham**.

PAGE 47   Cine-Madness

1. d   2. b   3. a   4. c   5. e

PAGE 48   In the Department Store

1. i   2. f   3. a   4. b   5. g   6. h   7. j   8. c   9. d   10. e

PAGE 49   Find It!

The things in the pictures are:
1. steps   3. a clock   5. a chair
6. goggles   7. a whistle   9. armbands
10. a lifeguard   12. a swimming cap
14. a swimsuit   20. a diving board

It's a **duck**.

PAGE 50   Exploring Nature

1. binoculars   2. compass   3. penknife
4. lighter   5. magnifying glass
6. camera   7. sunglasses   8. torch
9. money belt   10. flask

PAGE 51   Translate!

1. bill   2. petrol   3. trousers   4. holiday
5. pavement 6. biscuit   7. dustbin   8. films
9. sweets   10. curtains
a. 10; b. 1; c. 9; d. 7; e. 3; f. 8; g. 5; h. 6; i. 2; j. 4

PAGE 52   Spot the Country!

France Italy Spain Greece Austria Norway Sweden Ireland Hungary
Turkey

PAGE 53   What's the weather like?

Today it's **raining**.
1. raining; rainbow 2. cold; snowing 3. windy 4. cloudy; grey

PAGES 54 & 55   Holiday Weather

1. London   2. Northumbria   3. East Anglia   4. Wales
5. Cornwall 6. The Lake District 7. The Midlands

PAGES 56 & 57   Crossword

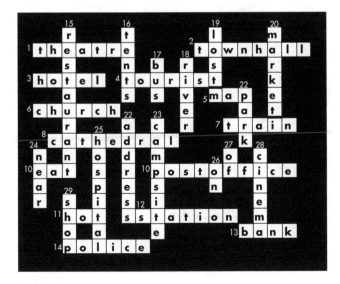

PAGE 58   A Day Out in London

1. Madame Tussaud's   2. Buckingham Palace
3. Tower Bridge   4. Trafalgar Square
5. Tower of London

PAGE 59   USA Quiz

one north   **six** south-east   **nineteen** east
eight north   **fourteen** west   **eleven** west
seventeen south **nine** east   **sixteen** north-east

PAGE 60   Picture Crossword

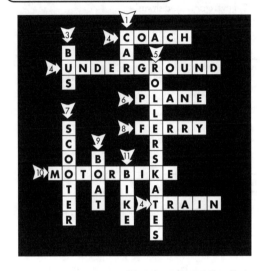

PAGE 61   Transport Puzzle

The correct choices will lead you through the letters
H-O-V-E-R-C-R-A-F-T: the mystery form of transport is **HOVERCRAFT**.

PAGE 62   Transport Quiz

1. b   2. b   3. a, b, d, f   4. b, f
1. e   2. d   3. b   4. a   5. c

PAGE 63   At the Railway Station

1. e;   2. c;   3. a;   4. g;   5. i;   6. h;   7. j;   8. f;   9. b;   10. d

PAGE 64   At the Airport

1. FOREIGN CURRENCY   2. INFORMATION
3. TOILETS   4. DEPARTURE GATES
5. CHECK-IN   6. LIFTS
7. PASSPORT CONTROL   8. ARRIVALS
9. LEFT LUGGAGE

The passenger is saying, '**I MISSED MY PLANE!**'

PAGE 65   Orienteering

They are going to meet at point **C**.

PAGE 66   Can You See?

The things in the pictures are:
2. a barn   3. a field   4. a river
6. a farmhouse   7. a road   8. a hill
9. a wood   10. a fox   11. a tractor

There's a **SCARECROW** in the middle of the field.

PAGE 67   Which Invention?

a. firework   b. skateboard   c. internet   d. lawn mower
e. hovercraft   f. dishwasher
1. lawn mower   2. hovercraft   3. dishwasher
4. skateboard   5. internet   6. firework

PAGE 68   Guess the Inventions!

1. iron   2. comb   3. umbrella
4. fax machine   5. alarm clock

1. towel   2. razor   3. mobile phone
4. vacuum cleaner   5. pencilcase

PAGE 69   Environmental Quiz

1. 200 litres   2. 50 litres   3. 1985   4. Between 18 and 48
kilometres   5. Because they contain CFC gas   6. 75   7. 45 kilos
8. 450 million   9. Unleaded petrol   10. Friends of the Earth

The name of the organization is **Greenpeace**.

PAGE 70   Hobbies A – Z

archery   judo   reading
ballet   knitting   singing
playing chess   learning a foreign   watching television
drawing   language   playing the ukelele
e-mailing friends   listening to music   video games
football   needlework   weight-lifting
playing the guitar   going to the opera   playing the xylophone
horse-riding   photography   doing yoga
surfing the internet doing quizzes   zzzzz (sleeping!)

PAGE 71   Summer Camp

canoeing   dancing   drama   fishing   judo
karaoke   quizzes   football rock-climbing   surfing
volleyball watching videos   windsurfing

Not pictured: fishing and football

PAGE 72   What's Your Ideal Holiday?

Students complete the quiz and check their score.

PAGE 73   Spot the Sport!

1. ice hockey   2. football   3. rugby   4. ice skating
5. basketball   6. cricket   7. skiing   8. judo
9. tennis   10. swimming 11. golf

Mystery sport is **horse-riding**.

PAGE 74   Sports Collocations

do: aerobics, gymnastics, taekwondo, yoga
go: jogging, skiing, horse-riding
play: snooker, baseball, volleyball, table tennis, hockey

PAGE 75   What are you watching?

1. cartoon   2. children's show   3. news
4. film   5. documentary   6. series
7. sports programme   8. talk show   9. gameshow

PAGE 76   Crazy Party!

A. 7   B. 1   C. 10   D. 9   E. 4
F. 5   G. 3   H. 2   I. 8   J. 6

PAGE 77   Musical Instruments

1. violin   2. recorder   3. cello   4. harp   5. flute
6. drums   7. trumpet   8. clarinet 9. piano
In an **orchestra**

PAGE 78   In the Pet Shop

1. j – tortoise   2. i – snake   3. g – rabbit
4. c – hamster   5. b – guinea pig   6. e – parrot
7. f – puppy   8. d – kitten   9. a – canary
10. h – goldfish

PAGE 79   Pairs

1. horse   2. turkey   3. donkey
4. sheep   5. bull   6. piglet
7. chicken   8. cockerel   9. rabbit
10. goose   11. duck   12. goat
13. lamb

PAGE 80   Anna's Diary

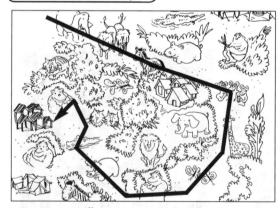

Anna stays at **Village A**.

PAGE 81   Animal Facts

1. true   2. false: elephant   3. true
4. false: cheetah   5. true   6. true
7. false: ostrich   8. true   9. true
10. false: koala   11. false   12. false: desert locust
13. true   14. false: Siberian tiger

The **cat** was the most scared animal.

PAGE 82   Christmas Cards

1. mince pies   2. decorations   3. Christmas pudding
4. roast turkey   5. Christmas cake   6. card
7. cracker   8. Christmas carol   9. Christmas tree
10. angel   11. bell   12. mistletoe
13. Father Christmas 14. chimney   15. present
16. reindeer   17. three kings   18. crib   19. star
20. snow

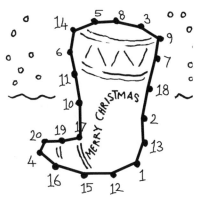

It's a **Christmas stocking**.

PAGE 83   Christmas Presents

1. trainers – Jane   2. video – Toby   3. chocolates – Chris
4. football – Rob   5. perfume – Sylvie   6. computer game – Mark
7. book –Julia   8. necklace – Lucy   9. board game – Mike
10. CD – Paul   11. jumper – Emma   12. sports bag – Nick

PAGE 84   Greetings!

1. C   2. F   3. A   4. E   5. B   6. D

1. Congratulations!   2. Happy Father's Day!
3. Good luck!   4. Goodbye!/Good luck!

PAGE 85   Holiday Souvenirs

a. sunglasses   b. postcard   c. teddy bear
d. flip-flops   e. straw hat   f. tea towel
g. pencil case   h. swimsuit   i. necklace
j. beach bag   k. coffee mug   l. T-shirt
m. fridge magnet   n. guide book

1. £14.75   2. £16.05   3. £11.40

PAGES 86 & 87   Seaside Holiday

No answer – game

PAGE 88   Holiday code

1. = G   2. = A   3. = S   4. = V   5.= B
6. = M   7. = N   8. = P   9. = U   10. = T
11. = O   12. = L   13. = I   14. = E   15. = C

Tom went to Scotland. Postcard A

Material written by: Sue Finnie and Danièle Bourdais

Commissioning Editor: Emma Grisewood

Content Editor: Cheryl Pelteret

Designer: Tracey Mason – TM.Designs

Cover Design: Eddie Rego

Illustrations by: Rachel Ball and Phil Burrows

Material in this publication may be photocopied,

but only for use by teachers and pupils within the purchasing institution.